Lecture Notes on
Fluid and Electrolyte
Balance

Dedicated to
Nicola, Steven and Ellen

Lecture Notes on Fluid and Electrolyte Balance

Sheila M. Willatts

MRCP FFARCS
Consultant Anaesthetist
Frenchay Hospital
Bristol

Blackwell Scientific Publications
OXFORD   LONDON   EDINBURGH
BOSTON   MELBOURNE

© 1982 by
Blackwell Scientific Publications
Editorial offices:
Osney Mead, Oxford OX2 0EL
8 John Street, London WC1N 2ES
9 Forrest Road, Edinburgh EH1 2QH
52 Beacon Street, Boston,
  Massachusetts 02108, USA
99 Barry Street, Carlton,
  Victoria 3053, Australia

First published 1982

Set by Southline Press Ltd.,
Littlehampton Road, Ferring, West
Sussex BN12 6PW

Printed and bound in Great Britain by
Billing and Sons Ltd., Guildford,
London, Oxford, Worcester

DISTRIBUTORS

USA
  Blackwell Mosby Book Distributors
  11830 Westline Industrial Drive
  St Louis, Missouri 63141

Canada
  Blackwell Mosby Book Distributors
  120 Melford Drive, Scarborough
  Ontario M1B 2X4

Australia
  Blackwell Scientific Book
  Distributors
  214 Berkeley Street, Carlton
  Victoria 3053

British Library
Cataloguing in Publication Data

Willatts, Sheila M.
  Lecture notes on fluid and electrolyte
  balance.
  1. Body fluids 2. Electrolyte
  metabolism
  I. Title
  612'01522   OP90.5

ISBN 0-632-008628

Contents

Preface

Fluid and electrolyte balance is a subject about which few wax lyrical. Cynics may state that our understanding in this difficult area has improved little over the last two decades. However, considerable advances have been made in our understanding of calcium and phosphate metabolism and technological advances now permit continuous recording of plasma electrolytes by intravascular ion selective electrodes. More practically parenteral nutrition for example can be undertaken scientifically and dialysis allows manipulation of total body water and electrolytes.

This book is not for the specialist. The first part outlines normal water and electrolyte balance and is concluded by tables of normal values. Part II considers disturbances from an essentially practical point of view concluding with a chapter on setting up infusion lines. The text is aimed at senior students and junior medical staff. Although much of the book is dogmatic some discussion is included on more recent aspects.

I am indebted to many colleagues at Frenchay Hospital and Bristol Royal Infirmary for advice, for reading and commenting on the text and in particular to my anaesthetic colleague Dr Frank Walters for his numerous helpful suggestions. I should like to thank the secretaries at Frenchay Hospital for initial typing and Peter Cox for providing illustrations. Special thanks are due to Norma Bryden who typed the final manuscript so efficiently and to Blackwell Scientific Publications for their help and encouragement during the writing of this book.

I hope that those who read it will subsequently take a greater interest in the management of fluid therapy in their patients.

The book is dedicated to my three children without whose help it would have been finished in half the time.

Sheila M. Willatts

Glossary of Terms

The International System of Units (SI, Système International) is in
widesread use in Great Britain and is adopted here. Those values
which are relevant in this book include:
  units of mass — kilogram (kg)
  amount of a substance — mole (mol)
  energy — joule
  pressure — pascal (Pa), kilopascal (kPa)
The preferred volume is a litre (l). Chemical analyses therefore
report mmol l^{-1} or μmol l^{-1}. Plasma proteins are still reported in g l^{-1}
and Hb as g per decilitre (g dl^{-1}).

ABBREVIATIONS

AA	amino acid	Cr	creatinine
ACD	acid citrate dextrose	CVP	central venous pressure
ADH	antidiuretic hormone	CVS	cardiovascular system
ARDS	adult respiratory	DPG	diphosphoglycerate
	distress syndrome	DVT	deep vein thrombosis
ARF	acute renal failure	ECF	extracellular fluid
ATP	adenosine triphosphate	ECG	electrocardiogram
ATPase	adenosine	EEG	electroencephalogram
	triphosphatase	FFA	free fatty acids
BP	blood pressure	g	gram
Ca	calcium	GFR	glomerular filtration rate
CCF	congestive cardiac	H	hydrogen
	failure	Hb	haemoglobin
Cl	chloride	HCO_3	bicarbonate
cm	centimetre	HD	haemodialysis
CO	cardiac output	Hg	mercury
CO_2	carbon dioxide	HPPF	human plasma protein
COP	colloid osmotic		fraction
	pressure	HPT	hyperparathyroidism
CPD	citrate phosphate	ICF	intracellular fluid
	dextrose	ISF	interstitial fluid

i.v.	intravenous	NH$_4$	ammonium
JVP	jugular venous pressure	O$_2$	oxygen
K	potassium	OH	hydroxyl
kg	kilogram	PCWP	pulmonary capillary wedge pressure
l	litre		
LAP	left atrial pressure	PD	peritoneal dialysis
LV	left ventricle	PO$_4$	phosphate
Mg	magnesium	PTH	parathormone
ml	millilitre	RA	right atrium
mm	millimetre	RNA	ribonucleic acid
MW	molecular weight	RV	right ventricle
N$_2$	nitrogen	SA	Sigaard–Anderson
Na	sodium	TBW	total body water
NH$_3$	ammonia		

PART I

Chapter 1
Normal Water Balance and Body Fluid Compartments

Water, water everywhere .... nor any drop to drink.

The Ancient Mariner
SAMUEL TAYLOR COLERIDGE

Water is indeed to be found everywhere in the human body. Without it survival is limited to a few days in the adult whereas total food deprivation is tolerated for at least a month. This fact is well known to surgeons and anaesthetists presented with patients who have advanced carcinoma of the oesophagus and severe dysphagia. There is no evidence for evolutionary adaptation to water deprivation in man. However the movement of vertebrates from a salt water to a fresh water environment leads to adaptive mechanisms in the distal tubule to protect the body from fatal dilution.

TOTAL BODY WATER

Total body water (TBW) constitutes 60% of body weight in the male and 52% of body weight in the female.

This difference is due to the higher fat content of females. About one third of this water is in the extracellular space; the other two thirds being intracellular.

Distribution of body water

Extracellular water constitutes approximately 20% of the body weight in both males and females. Therefore a 70 kg man will have:
TBW 42 litres.
Extracellular fluid (ECF) 14 litres.
Intracellular fluid (ICF) 28 litres.
Plasma volume 3.5 litres.

Plasma volume constitutes about 25% of ECF. Body water is passively distributed between ECF and ICF according to the osmolar content of each compartment.

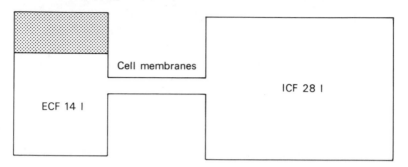

Fig. 1.1 Distribution of body water in a 70 kg man. The shaded area donates the intravascular compartment.

As water is highly polar it is an ideal biological solvent for polar compounds allowing stable dissociation of ions for intermediary metabolism. ECF is the transport medium for nutrients and waste products of metabolism whereas the water within cells is required for their structure, organisation and function. The monovalent ions, sodium and potassium are hydrated within the cell; each millimole binding 7 ml water. Intracellular water is not uniformly distributed. The highest concentration is present in metabolically active cells such as muscle, liver and kidney whilst the lowest concentration is found in inactive structures such as bone.

Methods of measurement of body water

Isotope dilution

The basis of this measurement lies in the injection of an isotope which will distribute completely throughout the compartment to be measured within a finite time after which its level (Cd) can be easily measured. During the measurement the subject must be in a stable metabolic state and allowance must be made for any excretion or metabolism which may occur during the equilibration period. If a given concentration of an isotope (Ci) is introduced into a fluid compartment in a volume (Vi) the distribution space (Vd) may be calculated at equilibrium thus:

$$Vd = \frac{Ci \times Vi}{Cd}$$

where Cd can be measured.

MEASUREMENT OF TOTAL BODY WATER

Deuterium oxide D_2O.
Tritium oxide.
Antipyrine.

Deuterium oxide is a stable compound which distributes itself as water throughout the body. It is not an isotope. Antipyrine is rarely used as it is not readily available in this country. Its main value is in circumstances when a scintillation counter is not available. Tritium oxide (^3H_2O) is an isotope of water and as such distributes throughout all compartments in the same way as water. After 3–4 hours mixing is good, metabolism is insignificant and urine losses are very small. Thus tritium oxide is the isotope of choice for this measurement. It is a weak beta-emitter with a biological half life of 10 days. The short biological half life makes it suitable for measurement in humans, although the radioactive (physical) half life is 12 years. 0.5 millicuries of ^3H_2O are injected and 4 hours allowed for normal equilibration although 6–8 hours may be required for the obese patient or those with ascites. The reproducibility of this method is usually ± 2%.

MEASUREMENT OF ECF VOLUME

Plasma volume. Three methods are available:
1 Evans blue dye is used to bind to plasma albumin.
2 Radioiodine is used to label serum albumin (RISA).
3 Labelled macroglobulin may be injected.

The disadvantage of the RISA method is the escape of 7–10% of the iodinated albumin per hour into interstitial fluid thereby causing an overestimate of plasma volume which becomes even greater in burns, trauma and ascites. This problem can be overcome to some extent by reducing the equilibration period.

ECF

1 Crystalloids: inulin, mannitol or sucrose. These are large molecules and therefore do not penetrate the entire ECF. Failure to penetrate areas such as the digestive tract and cerebrospinal fluid (CSF) will lead to an underestimation of the ECF volume.

2 Ionic substances: isotopes of chloride, bromide, sodium and sulphate.

These are smaller molecules but although they penetrate the entire ECF they may also penetrate cells and therefore over-estimate the ECF volume.

Studies of the disappearance of injected isotopes from the plasma suggests two rates of transfer:

(a) Transfer to a rapidly equilibrating pool in dynamic equilibrium with plasma (the functional ECF). This includes 25% of dense connective tissue and 10% of bone water. The volume of this compartment is 8.4 litres (l).

(b) Transfer to a slowly equilibrating pool over 24 hours. This pool includes the remaining connective tissue and bone.

MEASUREMENT OF INTERSTITIAL WATER

This is calculated by subtracting plasma volume from ECF volume.

MEASUREMENT OF RED CELL VOLUME

1 This may be calculated from the plasma volume and haematocrit.

2 The volume of distribution of reinjected red cells labelled with radioactive chromium (^{51}Cr) may be calculated.

MEASUREMENT OF INTRACELLULAR FLUID VOLUME

The volume of ICF cannot be measured directly. It is therefore calculated as follows:

$$ICF = TBW - ECF.$$

Such a calculated value will include the errors from both of the component measurements.

There is good correlation between ICF and total exchangeable potassium. Since potassium is the main intracellular cation its depletion leads to movement of water from the cells into ECF. Thus ICF volume depends on ECF osmolality such that a fall in ECF osmolality increases ICF volume since water enters the cells by osmosis (see below). ICF volume also depends on muscle mass and decreases with age.

Transcellular fluid

This is that part of the ECF which is formed by the transport activity of cells and includes secretions into the lumen of the gastrointestinal tract and the CSF.

The water content of body fluid compartments has been outlined so far without considering the solute content. Table 1.1 shows the mean ionic content of the body fluid compartments in mmol l^{-1}. The anion gap is explained in Chapter 13 but is included here for the sake of completeness.

Table 1.1 Mean ionic composition of body fluid compartments (mmol l^{-1})

Substance	Plasma	Interstitial fluid	Intracellular fluid
Sodium	141.00	144.00	10.00
Potassium	3.70	3.80	156.00
Chloride	102.00	115.00	3.00
Bicarbonate	28.00	30.00	10.00
Anion gap	15.00	0.00	0.00
Calcium	2.40	0.00	0.00
Magnesium	0.80	0.00	11.00
Phosphate	1.10	0.00	31.00
Protein	16.00	10.00	55.00

It is clear that there are striking differences in concentration of ions between compartments. This is further illustrated in Fig. 1.2. The most important factor maintaining separation of these compartments is the cell membrane: a complex structure consisting of lipids and proteins.

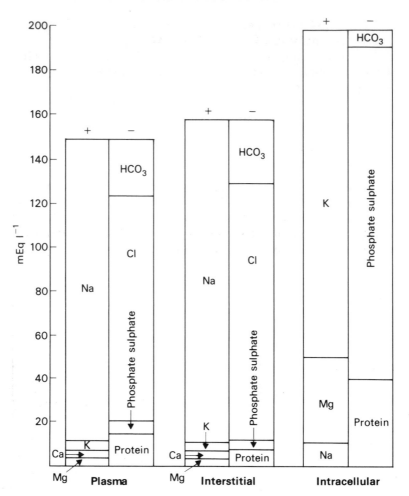

Fig. 1.2   Intracellular, interstitial and plasma electrolyte concentrations.

Despite the differences in ionic concentration between compartments, the law of electrical neutrality states that the sum of the negative charges of anions must be equal to the sum of positive charges of cations in any compartment. The ways in which regulation of fluid between compartments takes place will now be considered.

PHYSIOLOGICAL REGULATION OF
BODY FLUID COMPARTMENTS

The following factors are important:
1 Osmosis.
2 Diffusion.
3 Gibbs Donnan equilibrium.
4 Starling's forces.
5 Sodium pump.

Osmosis

This is the movement of solvent molecules across a selectively permeable membrane from a region of low solute concentration to a region of high solute concentration the membrane being impermeable to solute molecules.

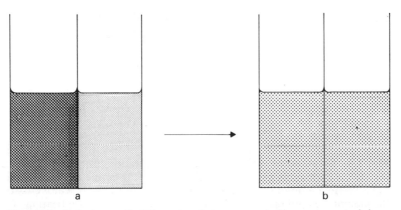

Fig. 1.3 Solutions of different solute concentrations separated by a permeable membrane. In a the solutions are separated by a permeable membrane and equilibrium takes place readily as shown in b.

It can be seen that equilibrium takes place until equal concentrations occur on either side of the membrane (b).

Biological membranes however are selectively permeable so that when solutions of different solute concentrations are separated solute molecules cannot equilibrate. Instead water passes from the region of low solute concentration (b in Fig. 1.4) to a region of high solute concentration.

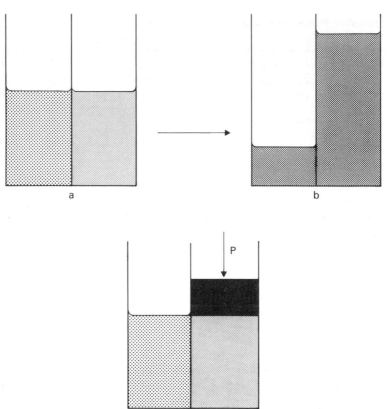

Fig. 1.4 Solutions of different solute concentration are separated by a selectively permeable membrane. a, The selectively permeable membrane separates two solutions of different solute concentrations; b, water crosses the membrane until the solute concentrations are equal; c, application of a pressure P which is the osmotic pressure will stop the movement of water (solvent) molecules across the membrane.

All cell membranes and capillary walls within the body are freely permeable to water. Hence all fluid compartments within the body must be isotonic with plasma, that is to say have the same osmotic pressure or osmolality as plasma (see below). Following an acute change in the composition of a fluid compartment equilibration rapidly occurs to restore isotonicity.

Osmolality and osmolarity

The osmotic activity of a substance in solution depends only on the number of discrete particles dissolved and *not* on the weight or valency. Hence a fully ionised substance will have double the osmotic effect of the same molar concentration of a substance in the unionised state.

OSMOLE

One osmole of a substance in ideal solution depresses the freezing point of a solvent, in this case water by 1.86°C. One milliosmole (mosmol) is one thousandth of an osmole.

One mole of any substance contains the same number of molecules, (Avagadro's number 6.061 $\times$ 10^{23}) and one mole = 1000 millimoles (mmol). A mole is the molecular weight (MW) of a substance in grams (g). A mole of an unionised substance is equal to an osmole but one mole of completely ionised sodium chloride equals two osmoles. In fact body fluids are not ideal solutions owing to interaction between ions.

OSMOLALITY

The osmolality of a solution is the number of osmoles of solute per kilogram of solvent. Clinically this is more usefully expressed as milliosmoles per kg (mosmol kg^{-1}).

OSMOLARITY

The osmolarity of a solution is the number of osmoles of solute per litre of *solution*. Hence it is temperature dependent.

This value may be calculated from plasma concentrations of electrolytes, glucose and urea. At least 17 formulae exist for calculation of osmolarity; one of the most acceptable is

$$2 \text{ (sodium + potassium) + glucose + urea}$$

all values being in mmol l^{-1}.

Values obtained in this way may be greater than measured osmolality as sodium chloride is only about 93% dissociated in plasma. Measured osmolality may exceed the calculated value in the presence of unmeasured osmotically active particles, for example mannitol and ethanol.

In an ideal solution the ratio of osmolality to molal concentration remains constant as the molar concentration changes. However, in practice the ratio increases as the solute concentration rises because of interaction between solute and solvent.

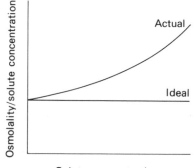

Fig. 1.5 A non ideal solution showing an apparent rise in osmolality with increasing solute concentration.

Methods of measurement of osmolality

1 Freezing point osmometers. These instruments depend on the principle that depression of freezing point of a solution is proportional to its total osmolal content.
2 Vapour pressure osmometers. The water vapour pressure of an aqueous solution varies with its osmolality. These instruments make use of this principle and are accurate to within $\pm$ 3 mosmol kg^{-1}. They can operate on very small samples (8 micro-litres).
  Normal plasma osmolality is 280–295 mosmol kg^{-1}.
  Urine osmolality varies from 300–1400 mosmol kg^{-1}.
An isotonic solution is one with the same osmolality as plasma. A hypotonic solution is one in which the osmolality is less than that of plasma. A hypertonic solution is one with an osmolality greater than that of plasma. If a measurement of osmolality is not available the calculated plasma osmolarity may be used. The difference between these two values is the osmolar gap and is usually 0–24 mosmol kg^{-1}. The osmolar gap may be raised in:
1 Ethanol intoxication. Ethanol depresses the freezing point of plasma water.

2 Multiple myeloma and other hyperproteinaemic states.
3 Hyperlipoproteinaemia.

In these last two conditions the percentage of plasma solids is raised from the normal 7% so that although the concentration of electrolytes in plasma water is normal (that is to say, the osmolality is normal) the percentage of the plasma that is really water is reduced. Thus there is a reduction in calculated osmolarity.

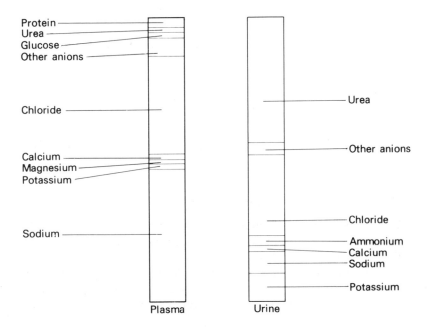

Fig. 1.6 Constituents of plasma and urine.

Urine constituents vary widely especially during illness so that calculations for urine osmolarity are very prone to error. However, in the absence of a measured osmolality the measured specific gravity, which is the weight of a solution compared to the weight of water, is of some help. In the absence of hyperglycaemia, proteinuria or excretion of radiological contrast media the relationship shown in Table 1.2 applies.

Table 1.2   Relationship between urine specific gravity and osmolality.

Specific gravity	Osmolality
1.010	350
1.020	700
1.030	1050

ECF OSMOLALITY

The main determinent of ECF osmolality is its sodium concentration. If ECF sodium concentration and hence osmolality rises water will be withdrawn from cells to re-establish equal osmolality (isotonicity). Conversely acute hyponatraemia will increase intracellular water regardless of the level of total body water. Sodium is unique as a solute in that changes in its concentration are more often due to changes in the volume of its solvent (water) than in total sodium stores.

ICF OSMOLALITY

The main determinant of ICF osmotic pressure is the intracellular potassium concentration. Some intracellular ions may be osmotically inactive. 30% of intracellular magnesium is bound to lipoproteins, ribonucleic acid (RNA) and adenosine triphosphate (ATP).

It is not clear whether intracellular potassium or extracellular sodium is the prime controller of body osmolality.

COLLOID OSMOTIC PRESSURE

Measurement of plasma osmolality is almost entirely a measure of crystalloid osmolality. Only about 0.5% of the total plasma osmolality is attributable to colloid. Colloids are large protein molecules with a molecular weight greater than 30 000. This small percentage however is very important since capillaries are only minimally permeable to colloids which therefore have an important effect of 'holding' water within the plasma compartment and maintaining water distribution between body fluid compartments. A fall in colloid osmotic pressure is an important aetiological factor in the development of pulmonary oedema. Normal colloid osmotic pressure (COP) is 20–25 mmHg being greater in the ambulant than in the supine patient. This COP is largely attributable to plasma proteins although the correlation between plasma albumin and COP under stable conditions is unreliable.

Recently developed machines for colloid osmotic pressure measurement (oncometers) utilise semipermeable membranes and electronic pressure transducers to measure COP on small samples of fluid.

Diffusion

Simple diffusion permits passage of a substance along a chemical gradient. Cell membranes have a high lipid content hence lipophilic and unionised substances will cross membranes at a faster rate than hydrophilic, polar or ionised substances. Diffusion is facilitated by pores in cell membranes of 0.7 nanometres diameter. The rate of diffusion of a substance does not depend on its atomic weight but its hydrated radius that is to say its size when hydrated with water molecules.

Gibbs Donnan equilibrium

ICF contains more anionic protein molecules than does interstitial fluid. This results in an increase in diffusible cations (sodium, potassium) and a decrease in diffusible anion (chloride) and means that the total number of diffusible ions is greater in ICF (see Fig. 1.2).

Starling's forces

In an adult the capillary bed provides 6300 square metres of filtering surface. Plasma protein osmotic pressure (OP) is about 25 mmHg whereas blood pressure is 35 mmHg at the arterial end of the capillary and 15 mmHg at the venous end. This results in diffusion of water and diffusible ions out of the capillary and into the interstitial fluid at the arterial end of the capillary and reabsorption of about 90% of this at the venous end.

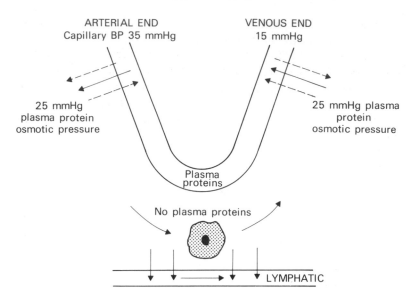

Fig. 1.7 Transport of water in the capillary circulation.

Total flow of water from the interstitial fluid is 20 l daily in an adult. Normal interstitial fluid pressure is about 7 mmHg sub-atmospheric. Normally lymphatics drain excess fluid from the interstium and lymph flow can increase dramatically if the interstitial fluid is rapidly expanded.

Sodium pump

The nondiffusible intracellular proteins tend to draw water into cells. Sodium (Na) tends to enter the cell by diffusion from a high ECF to a low ICF concentration. This tendency is offset by the sodium pump which is located in the cell membrane and actively extrudes Na from the cell into ECF. The sodium pump depends on a supply of ATP. It is very temperature sensitive and is inhibited by cardiac glycosides. A similar, linked mechanism exists for transport of potassium (K) ions in the opposite direction.

The sick cell syndrome occurs in a variety of situations such as hypoxia and septicaemia when the function of the sodium pump breaks down, Na enters the cell and K is lost from the cell into plasma. The ions move down their chemical concentration gradients. Plasma Na falls and plasma K rises.

As a result of unequal distribution of ions across membranes a potential difference of 10–100 millivolts is set up across the cell membrane with the inside negative to the outside. This potential difference is closely related to the difference in K concentration across the membrane and may be described by the Nernst Planck equation.

This assumes that at the resting potential of biological membranes permeability to sodium and to chloride is zero.

$$V = \frac{RT}{F} \log_e \frac{Ko}{Ki}$$

V = Potential difference
R = The gas constant
F = Faraday's constant
T = Temperature
Ko = Concentration of potassium in the ECF
Ki = Concentration of potassium in the ICF.

Total body water content is finely regulated. Any attempt at parenteral repletion of body fluids requires a good working knowledge of the basic normal physiological control of water balance.

WATER BALANCE

An average daily water requirement in adults is approximately 1500 ml m^{-2}. Sufficient water must be supplied to replace insensible losses and excrete solute products of metabolism.

Water intake

1 Oral fluids.
2 The water content of food. Melon and citrus fruits contain about 90% water.
3 Metabolism. Oxidation of food to carbon dioxide and water provides 300–500 ml of water daily (120 ml per 1000 calories). Water is absorbed in response to the osmotic pressure difference between plasma and intestinal contents. At any one time about

1.5% of body water lies within the gastrointestinal tract with food and electrolytes. Most gastrointestinal contents are isotonic although saliva is hypotonic.

Water loss

1   Urine. Urine volume is very variable but on average amounts to 1500 ml per day. A minimum volume of 500 ml in an adult is necessary to eliminate the normal solute load for excretion.
2   Insensible loss. This amounts to 0.5 ml kg^{-1} hour^{-1} at 37°C (840 ml in 24 hours in a 70 kg man). Evaporation occurs from the skin and water vapour is lost into expired air.
3   Faeces 100–200 ml daily.

This simple outline of water balance takes no account of pathological processes which will be dealt with in subsequent chapters. Individual factors vary greatly from day to day. Muscular work and fever produce a marked increase in water loss. Sweating occurs from sweat glands controlled by the sympathetic nervous system from the hypothalamic heat regulating centre. A hot environment and muscular activity increase sweat production. In hot climates up to 3 litres of water per hour may be lost as sweat. Evaporation of this sweat will increase heat loss (latent heat of vaporisation). Salicylate poisoning, thyrotoxicosis and other factors which increase metabolism will also increase water loss.

Two simple measurements may help in elucidating the water balance problems in an adult:
1   Weigh the patient. Acute changes in weight are likely to be due to changes in water balance. Starvation is considered in later chapters.
2   Check that the urine volume is greater than 1 litre in 24 hours.

Regulation of water balance

Happily for humans osmotic homeostasis can be maintained over a wide range of water intake provided the following are normal:
1   Renal function.
2   Renal blood supply.
3   Hormonal activity.
The fact that many patients come to no harm and some even do well following very varied, often inappropriate intravenous fluid

regimes prescribed by well intentioned medical staff probably reflects the normal ability of the kidney to vary the solute excretion to maintain normal plasma osmolality. Daily water turnover depends on osmolar production and renal concentrating ability. Fine regulation of water balance keeps plasma omsolality between 280 and 295 kg⁻¹. Under normal circumstances daily water requirements are 30 ml kg⁻¹. The minimum water intake is that which is required to replace loss from all body sources and the maximum intake is that which can be excreted by the kidney.

$$\text{Minimum urine output} = \frac{\text{osmolar load (mosmol per day)}}{\text{renal concentrating ability}}$$
$$\text{(mosmol l}^{-1}\text{)}$$

Normally this is $\frac{600}{1200} = 0.5$ litres per day

In health the possible range of water intake is very wide before any disturbance occurs but in the ill, hypercatabolic patient the range may be small owing to an increased solute load, excess losses, impaired renal function, falling cardiac output and the hormonal imbalance of the stress response. In such a patient the osmolar load may rise to 1000 mosmol per day and concentrating ability may be reduced to 800 mosmol l⁻¹.

Minimal urine output then becomes $\frac{1000}{800} = 1.25$ l per day

In addition to this increased minimum urine output, fever will increase insensible water loss.

Variations in water intake or loss produce a small plasma osmotic change which activates regulatory mechanisms via the hypothalamus affecting thirst and urine concentration.

Thirst

Thirst is more important than urine concentration in preventing dehydration due to water deprivation or due to the hyperosmolality of an increased solute load. The more usual circumstance is that water intake is in excess of needs, and this excess water is excreted by the kidney.

ROLE OF THE KIDNEY IN WATER EXCRETION

The renal glomeruli produce 120 ml per minute of filtrate from plasma (180 l over 24 hours). In the case of water 99% of this will be reabsorbed as the filtrate passes through the tubule thereby producing about 1.5 l of urine per day. Normally there is a wide range of urine osmolality such that the same solute load can be excreted in 500 ml of urine with an osmolality of 1400 mosmol kg^{-1} or in 23.3 l of urine with an osmolality of 30 mosmol kg^{-1}.

Table 1.3   Range of urine volume.

	Osmolar production (mosmol daily)	Maximum urine osmolality (mosmol kg^{-1})	Minimum urine osmolality (mosmol kg^{-1})	Maximum urine volume (1)	Minimum urine volume (1)
Healthy	600	1200	30	20	0.5
Hypercatabolic	1200	1200	30	40	1
Postoperative on 2 litres of 5% dextrose daily	200	600	200	1	0.3

Table 1.3 illustrates the wide range of urine volume possible under different clinical circumstances.

Countercurrent multiplier

A countercurrent system is responsible for producing a concentrated urine. A gradient of increasing osmolality exists as one progresses along the tubule more deeply into the medulla.

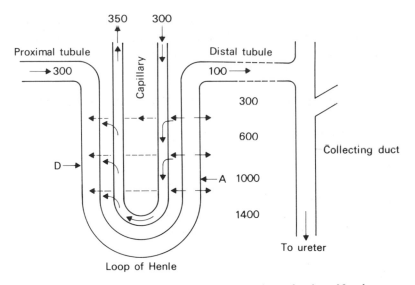

Fig. 1.8 Countercurrent system for production of urine. Numbers = osmolality; D = descending limb; A = ascending limb.

25% of filtered Na is reabsorbed between the end of the proximal tubule and the beginning of the distal tubule whereas less than 15% of filtered water is reabsorbed in this region. Therefore more salt is reabsorbed than water and dilute fluid is present at the end of the distal tubule. The rate of salt reabsorption in the loop of Henle varies with the sodium load presented to it by the proximal tubule. Recently it has been shown that Na reabsorption in the ascending limb of the loop of Henle is due mainly to active transport of chloride (Cl) ions. This renders the lumen of the tubule electrically positive (3–9 mV) with respect to the peritubular fluid. Therefore Na diffuses out *passively* along the electrical and chemical gradient. This segment of the loop of Henle is virtually impermeable to water. Na diffuses passively into the descending limb and is carried round again to the ascending limb where the process is repeated. The blood in the accompanying capillary also takes part in this exchange. Na concentration increases as blood flows through the hypertonic medulla and it decreases again when the capillary leaves the area of high osmolality.

The countercurrent mechanism depends on the hairpin structure of the loops of Henle and the high concentration of Na, Cl and urea in the depths of the medulla. The collecting ducts act as a source of urea to add to the interstitial hypertonicity. This mechanism depends on two factors:

1 Complete solute impermeability of the descending limb of the loop of Henle.

2 Permeability of the ascending limb to Na, Cl and urea but NOT to water.

Therefore fluid in the descending limb becomes concentrated by removal of water, and fluid in the ascending limb is diluted by net *loss* of salt in excess of the net gain of urea by passive diffusion. Very important for this concept is the composition of the interstitial fluid, that is to say, a mixture of hyperosmotic concentrations of salt AND urea. Fluid in the descending limb of the loop of Henle contains only salt as the osmotically active component (Figs. 1.9, 1.11).

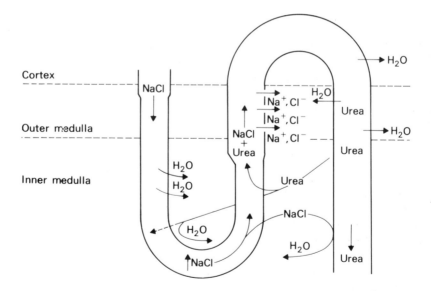

Fig. 1.9 Countercurrent concentrating mechanism.

Fluid entering the lower ascending limb contains sodium chloride at higher concentration than the surrounding fluid which has the same osmotic pressure but due to *urea + salt*. Therefore in this segment there is net *outward* diffusion of NaCl and inward diffusion of urea down their respective concentration gradients. More salt must be lost than urea gained because fluid at the distal end of the loop is hypotonic to plasma. The general view is that transport of NaCl out of this thin ascending limb is the *active* step in counter-current multiplication.

ROLE OF UREA

When urea is the principal constituent of urine the volume of urine required to excrete a given solute load is reduced. Urea clearance is always less than glomerular filtration rate (GFR) and is independent of the plasma urea over a wide range of concentration. Urea clearance depends on urine flow (fractional water reabsorption). The mechanism for this is the recycling of urea from the medullary collecting ducts into the loops of Henle and is made possible by the almost continuous reabsorption of water along the nephron. Urea transport is passive and as water is reabsorbed urea becomes more concentrated and this is maximal in the medullary collecting ducts. This effect is augmented by an antidiuresis. Even at high antidiuretic hormone (ADH) levels the permeability of collecting ducts and distal tubules to urea is low, therefore increased water reabsorption very effectively progressively raises the urea concentration of fluid entering the medullary collecting ducts. More urea is reabsorbed in the medulla at low urine flows when hypertonic urine is formed than at high urine flows. The reabsorbed urea diffuses into the medullary interstitum and vasa recta until its concentration is nearly the same at any given level as in the collecting duct.

Urea constitutes 40–50% of the total solute concentration of the medullary interstitial fluid during antidiuresis and 10% during a water diuresis.

A high urea in glomerular filtrate therefore promotes increased urinary concentration of non-urea solutes. The urea induced passive concentration of salt in the descending limb and increased outflow of salt from the ascending limb into the interstitium augments a single passive effect in this segment. Therefore a rise in medullary salt concentration is achieved leading to increased water reabsorption from collecting ducts and hence an increase in non-urea solutes in the urine. The concentrations of Na and urea in the interstitium are kept high by the slow blood flow in the vasa recta.

ADH may contribute to concentration of urine not only by enhancing the permeability of the distal tubule but also by enhancing the transport of salt and urea into the medullary interstitium to increase the osmotic gradient.

An efficient countercurrent system depends on:

1   A good glomerular filtration rate. A reduction in GFR of 25% will reduce concentrating ability significantly because of inadequate delivery of Na and urea to the tubule. Sufficient sodium chloride must be available to the ascending limb active transport system to maintain the hypertonicity in the medulla.

2   If the solute load is increased this has the effect of washing out medullary osmoles and reduces the time the multiplier has to work. In these circumstances both concentrating and diluting ability are affected. Flow rate in the collecting ducts is increased and diluting ability reduced. This is illustrated in Fig. 1.10. Osmotic diuretics effectively increase the solute load.

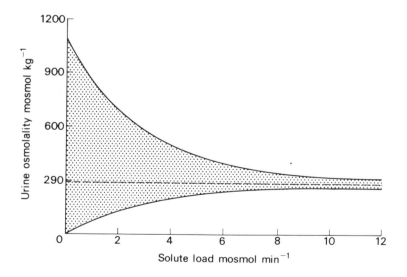

Fig. 1.10   The effect of solute load on urine osmolality.

Osmotic diuresis

A solute such as mannitol that is not reabsorbed in the proximal tubule exerts a considerable osmotic effect. As its concentration in the tubule rises large volumes of isotonic fluid are presented to the countercurrent mechanism. More fluid passes through the loops, the hyperosmolality of the medullary pyramids is reduced and less water is subsequently reabsorbed from the collecting ducts.

It has already been stated that daily fluid intake exceeds requirements so that the kidney is usually required to excrete the excess water.

Free water

The kidney can excrete water in excess of that required to render the urine isotonic as we have seen above, provided the secretion of antidiuretic hormone can be suppressed. Such excess water excretion is termed *free water*. If excess ADH is secreted as in the metabolic response to trauma (see Chapter 9) which overrides normal osmoreceptor regulation, then any free water will be reabsorbed in the distal tubule and collecting duct. In these circumstances the only route of free water excretion is through the lungs and skin.

WATER DEPRIVATION

The opposite situation of water deprivation or increased solute intake produces thirst.

Thirst

Thirst sensitive areas exist in the ventromedial and anterior areas of the hypothalamus. This area is closely associated with nuclei regulating ADH secretion. Therefore if water is withheld:
1   A sensation of thirst occurs.
2   ADH is secreted.
3   Food intake is inhibited.
Thirst increases water ingestion in the conscious patient. This water moves freely across the mucosa of the small and large intestine and to a lesser extent across the gastric mucosa. If a large amount of

hypotonic fluid is ingested in the absence of water depletion, water diuresis occurs after 15 minutes. This represents the time required for absorption of the water and inhibition of ADH secretion. The diuresis is maximal at about 40 minutes after ingestion. Maximum urine flow during a water diuresis is about 16 ml min^{-1}.

Osmoreceptors

The osmoreceptor area in the hypothalmus can detect a 1% change in body osmolality which in an adult is roughly equivalent to a change of 350 ml. Two mechanisms by which this detection may occur are:

1 Sensing a change in cell volume due to water depletion.
2 Sensing the ECF solute load.

In addition to this mechanism acting in close association with ADH there are others nonosmotic factors which are important in regulation of water balance (Table 1.4). If the effective ECF volume is severely depleted for example in intestinal obstruction this will override osmolality and produce fluid retention. If the cardiac output falls or intravascular volume depletion results in hypotension this is detected by intrathoracic, carotid sinus and aortic baroreceptors, and mechanisms to increase blood pressure including fluid retention are stimulated. The renin angiotensin system is also activated and will result in sodium retention. These factors are discussed more fully in later chapters. In febrile states water

Table 1.4 Factors affecting thirst and ADH secretion.

Osmotic
Water depletion
Osmolar load

Nonosmotic
Volume receptors:
   arterial — carotid, aortic
   venous — left atrial, pulmonary venous
Temperature
Hypoxia

The normal diurnal rhythm of ADH secretion

requirements are increased. Hypoxia impairs tissue perfusion and oxygenation which may result in impaired cell membrane activity (the sick cell syndrome) and fluid retention.

Antidiuretic hormone

This is the most important hormone concerned with water balance. It is nonapeptide with molecular weight 1084 and is synthesised in the supraoptic and paraventricular nuclei of the hypothalamus. It travels in vesicles with carrier protein (neurophysin I) to the posterior pituitary whence it is discharged into capillaries. ADH acts on the distal tubule and collecting duct as has already been discussed, permitting increased reabsorption of water. Regulation of ADH secretion results in a range of urine osmolality (30–1200 mosmol kg^{-1}). A change in plasma osmolality of 1 mosmol kg^{-1} alters urine osmolality by 95 mosmol kg^{-1} by the ADH mechanism.

The normal pituitary content of ADH is 30 micrograms and its plasma half life is 16–20 minutes. At a plasma osmolality below 280 mosmol kg^{-1} ADH levels are undetectable. Within the normal range of plasma osmolality the full range of urine osmolality occurs with small changes in plasma ADH (0.4–5 pg ml^{-1}). The highest normal plasma osmolality (295 mosmol kg^{-1}) maximally stimulates ADH secretion, coincides with maximum urine osmolality and also stimulates thirst. As plasma osmolality rises from 280–295 mosmol kg^{-1} urine volume falls 10–20 times.

The osmoreceptor response to solutes is selective, that is to say, it is effective osmolality which is being regulated.

1   Glucose, urea and ethanol which readily cross the blood brain barrier do *not* stimulate ADH release although they increase plasma osmolality. In clinical hyperglycaemic states therefore the poor ADH response may aggravate polyuria and dehydration (see Chapter 14).

2   Sodium and mannitol which penetrate the blood brain barrier slowly are potent stimuli of ADH release. Therefore it is the gradient of osmolality between cells and ECF that stimulates ADH secretion or the reduction in cell volume which occurs as water moves out of the cell to restore isotonicity.

In summary therefore regulation of ADH is mainly by osmotic stimuli but nonosmotic factors can affect the threshold for release and sensitivity of the response.

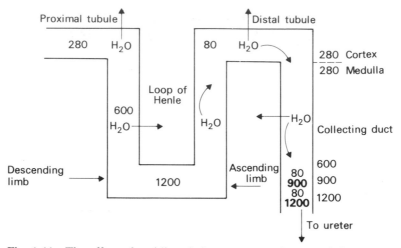

Fig. 1.11 The effect of antidiuretic hormone on urine osmolality. Numbers show osmolality (mosmol kg^{-1}); bold type = with ADH; medium type = without ADH.

Other hormones affecting renal water secretion

1 Catecholamines. Beta effects increase ADH release by a baroreceptor effect. Alpha effects reduce ADH release.

2 Thyroxine increases diluting capacity because of an increase in distal tubular sodium reabsorption or a reduction in ADH release.

3 Glucocorticoids increase ADH release.

4 Mineralocorticoids reduce diluting capacity. Nonosmotic stimuli may still cause ADH release.

5 Angiotensin has a variable response.

6 Prostaglandins have the following effects:

(a) Enhance the action of ADH

(b) Increase ADH release by a baroreceptor effect

(c) Decrease concentrating ability by a reduction in medullary osmoles.

It is extremely difficult to separate water balance from sodium balance although an attempt has been made to do so. It is also difficult to discuss electrolyte balance in isolation from acid base regulation. Changes in total body water are reflected in altered plasma sodium concentration. Throughout this book changes will as far as possible be considered under the primary abnormality although inevitably some repetition will be necessary.

Chapter 2
Normal Sodium and Chloride Balance

Ye are the salt of the earth
Saint Matthew (Chapter 13)

Total body sodium (Na) varies between the sexes.
In the adult male it is 52–60 mmol kg^{-1}.
In the adult female it is 48–55 mmol kg^{-1}.
Therefore a 70 kg man contains 3600–4200 mmol Na. Since ECF (interstitial fluid plus plasma) forms about 20% of total body weight and extracellular Na concentration is 133–145 mmol l^{-1} then about 2000 mmol (50% of the total body Na) exists in the extracellular compartment. About 40% of the total body Na is found in the skeleton where 75% of it is very slowly if ever exchanged with that in other body fluids as it is absorbed on to hydroxyapatite crystals in dense bone (non-exchangeable Na pool).

Sodium therefore is the major extracellular cation. Intracellular Na concentration is low and varies between cell types:
3–4 mmol l^{-1} in muscle cells.
20 mmol l^{-1} in red blood cells.

EXCHANGEABLE SODIUM (Na$_e$)

This represents 65–70% of total body Na:
In females it comprises 41.7 mmol kg^{-1} body weight.
In males it comprises 40.1 mmol kg^{-1} body weight.
Exchangeable Na is made up of:
1 Extracellular Na.
2 Intracellular Na.
3 40–50% of total bone sodium.

It is this value that is measured by isotope dilution. ^{24}Na or ^{22}Na may be used for this purpose. There is considerable individual variation in Na_e and again values are higher in males than in females. Exchangeable Na from bone may partly replace Na lost from the ECF. As Na is the major ECF cation it contributes 86% of ECF osmolality (normally 280–295 mosmol kg^{-1}). Potassium plays a similar role in the ICF which is a much larger volume than the ECF. We have already seen that changing the osmolality in one body compartment is rapidly dealt with by the passage of water across cell membranes to produce isotonicity (see p. 7).

Administration of a large water load

If a large water load is administered into the circulation, it produces the following effects:
1   Plasma and interstitial osmolality are reduced.
2   Water leaves the ECF and enters cells.
3   Isotonicity is restored.
ICF volume is much larger than ECF volume, so that only a small increase in ECF volume will occur relative to the volume of water administered.

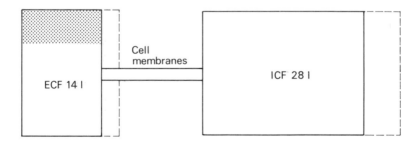

Fig. 2.1   The result of administration of a large water load. The dotted lines show the effect of a 10 litre water load. As water distributes freely between compartments osmolality is equally reduced in ECF and ICF. The shaded area denotes the intravascular compartment.

Administration of hypertonic saline

If hypertonic saline is infused into the circulation, the following effects are produced:

(a) Plasma and interstitial fluid osmolality increase.
(b) Water then leaves the ICF and enters ECF.
(c) Isotonicity is restored.

The administered saline has stayed in the ECF but water has been added to maintain osmolality and the ECF has therefore been rapidly expanded at the expense of the ICF.

Loss of water without loss of solute

This is a rare situation and leads to reduction in the volume of ECF and ICF.

Loss of solute without water

Loss of solute from the ECF leads to a fall in osmolality with consequent passage of water from ECF to ICF, which may lead to swelling of cells. This situation will occur as administered glucose is metabolised to carbon dioxide and water, in effect water has been infused into the intravascular volume.

MEASUREMENT OF PLASMA SODIUM

There are two main methods: flame photometry and ion selective electrodes.

Flame photometry

Flame emission photometry

If a solution containing Na is squirted into a flame, a small number of atoms absorb energy so that one of the electrons moves further from the nucleus to a position of higher energy. As these atoms return to their original state they emit energy as light of specific wavelength. The amount of light emitted is proportional to the concentration of Na. Most machines compare this with an internal reference element (usually lithium).

Atomic absorption photometry

This is a more sensitive technique for research purposes.

Ion selective electrodes

Sodium glass electrode

When this electrode is in contact with a plasma sample a potential difference is set up proportional to the concentration of Na in the plasma. Very small volumes of plasma are required and the same system may be used for urine Na estimation. It is important that blood for plasma Na estimation is taken from a fasting, recumbent patient and from a limb with no intravenous infusion running, ideally without recourse to a tourniquet.

Plasma Na reflects the ratio between total ICF Na and extracellular water. An abnormal plasma Na therefore may be due to changes in either or both of these. There is a relationship between plasma Na and exchangeable Na and potassium.

$$\text{Na plasma } \alpha \quad \frac{\text{Na}_e + \text{K}_e}{\text{TBW}}$$

NORMAL PLASMA SODIUM

The range for this value is 133–145 mmol l^{-1}.

Interpretation of this measured result

Hyponatraemia may be present in salt depletion or overload. This matter is discussed more fully in Chapter 6. There is no correlation between plasma and total body Na. Falsely low Na levels may occur if blood is taken near a vein with a hypotonic infusion running or if plasma contains excess lipid or protein.

The main difference between interstitial fluid and plasma is the protein content of the latter. Protein constitutes 6% of plasma volume but only 1% of interstitial fluid volume. Since Na is dissolved in the aqueous phase only, it might be expected that plasma Na would be less than interstitial fluid (ISF) Na whereas when measured in practice they are the same.

GIBBS DONNAN EFFECT

1   Protein is a non-diffusible anion present in plasma but insignificantly in interstitial fluid.

2 Since electrical neutrality must be maintained the diffusible ions must distribute *unequally* across the capillary membrane so that the total number of cations equals the total number of anions on each side.

3 Within the capillary containing non-diffusible protein anion the concentration of diffusible anions must be less than outside the capillary (ISF) and the concentration of cations must be more.

4 Effectively therefore, diffusible anions such as chloride are in lower concentration in plasma than ISF and diffusible cations such as Na are in higher concentration ($6-7$ mmol l^{-1} greater) in plasma than in ISF.

However, Na concentration is measured in mmol l^{-1} of plasma *not* per litre plasma water and hence achieves a value almost identical to that in ISF (see Fig. 1.2).

Pseudohyponatraemia

Sodium is present only in the aqueous phase of plasma so that if plasma contains an abnormal amount of lipid contracting the water volume then the measured sodium will be spuriously low.

Such a situation exists in nephrotic syndrome and diabetes mellitus. If in 1 litre of plasma there are 800 ml water and 200 ml lipid with a measured Na of 120 mmol l^{-1} then the calculated true plasma sodium is 150 mmol l^{-1}. This phenomenon may have dangerous results if not recognised and if an inappropriate sodium load is given to correct the hyponatraemia. Measurement of urine sodium may help to diagnose this situation. In true hyponatraemia urine Na and Cl will be low. This topic is further discussed in Chapter 6. Use of an ion selective electrode which measures activity of ions in plasma water overcomes this problem to a large extent being relatively unaffected by increases in lipids or proteins which reduce the plasma water space. Such machines are of considerable help provided they do *not* dilute the plasma before presenting it to the electrode.

SODIUM BALANCE

Intake

1 Food. **2** Drinks. **3** Added salt with food.

Obviously the intake is very variable depending on diet and taste. Most of the daily Na intake is due to added salt with meals, hence restricted Na diets are not difficult to plan. The highlanders of New Guinea consume less than 10 mmol per day and remain healthy, as do a small number of people consuming up to 200 mmol of Na daily. Optimum intake however is about 75 mmol per day. 70–100 mmol daily of Na are suggested as a baseline replacement. If Na intake is very low minor disturbances of gastrointestinal function may lead to hyponatraemia and dehydration. This is akin to being at the edge of a precipice. The true minimum Na intake should probably be 20 mmol daily.

Output

1   Faeces and skin. 5–10 mmol Na are lost daily by these routes.
2   Sweat. Under normal circumstances the losses are small (less than 25 mmol daily). In the presence of fever and visible sweating due to muscular activity at high environmental temperature losses may be much higher.
3   Urine. The kidney normally maintains Na balance by excreting all the Na which is in excess of requirements. The normal kidney can probably excrete over 300 mmol Na daily except in Na retention states. In conditions of salt loss or deprivation, however, it is very efficient in conserving Na and then daily urinary losses may be only 1 mmol l^{-1} after a few days. On an average Western diet urine K:Na ratio is 1:2.

The renal regulation of salt balance is not an immediate phenomenon so that small daily differences may occur between intake and output. Large fluctuations in salt intake may require 3–5 days for the kidney to establish a new steady state of Na output.

MEASUREMENT OF URINE SODIUM

This is becoming increasingly common in ill patients. However, the value of such measurements must be interpreted with caution. An isolated urine Na measurement is of very limited value as it is dependent on dietary Na and recently administered diuretics, the normal range is very wide. This is discussed more fully in Chapter 6. A 24 hour urine Na may demonstrate the renal ability to excrete Na and a low urine Na in oliguric states indicates a low perfusion state.

NORMAL REGULATION OF SODIUM BALANCE

We have seen that Na intake is very variable depending on diet and taste, how then is excretion regulated to compensate for variable losses via the gastrointestinal tract and sweat? This is effected by the kidney. There is some evidence that a gut hormone may be involved. Administration of hypertonic saline orally is associated with a much higher rate of excretion of Na than administration of an equivalent dose intravenously.

RENAL REGULATION OF SODIUM BALANCE

The glomeruli within the kidney filter plasma, allowing water and electrolytes but not protein, through into the tubule. The working of the countercurrent multiplier has been considered in Chapter 1. Glomerular filtrate ressembles plasma initially but during its course through the tubule large amounts of water and variable amounts of electrolyte are reabsorbed so that by selective active and passive control mechanisms the renal tubule controls electrolyte balance within the body. In addition to reabsorption, tubular secretion is important for electrolytes such as potassium.

There is still no convincing demonstration of any Na receptor in the body nor much evidence of how the Na status of the body is relayed to the kidney. How then does the kidney detect changes in body Na content? The mechanism is likely to include changes in ECF volume in the following way.

When ECF volume falls the distending pressure in the large arteries and carotid sinus falls; arterial blood pressure may also fall. As ECF volume falls the sympathetic nervous system is reflexly stimulated, which produces the following:

1 Catecholamine induced increase in cardiac output.
2 Peripheral constriction, especially in skin, splanchnic and renal vessels.
3 Stimulation of the renin angiotensin system.

The kidney therefore may be affected by changes in its blood pressure or blood supply mediated by the mechanisms listed above. Other volume receptors in addition to the carotid sinus are found in the left atrium, the right atrium and juxtamedullary apparatus. Volume expansion stimulates both the high and low pressure baro-receptors to increase Na excretion by a mechanism independent of the constitution of the blood. There are three possibilities for relay of information from the baroreceptors to the kidney:

1 Circulating natriuretic hormone.
2 Dopamine.
3 Decreased renal nerve activity.

CONTROL OF SODIUM EXCRETION

1 Glomerular filtration rate (GFR).
2 Aldosterone.
3 Third factor (natriuretic hormone).

GFR

Reduction in GFR reduces urinary Na excretion and vice versa. This mechanism can, however, be overridden. In animals a large salt load given in the presence of an experimental reduction in GFR will still produce a marked Na diuresis (natriuresis). Renal nervous activity is one factor controlling GFR.

Aldosterone

This mineralocorticoid hormone is secreted by the zona glomerul-osa of the adrenal cortex. It stimulates renal tubular reabsorption of Na and decreases the Na content of sweat. Aldosterone release is stimulated by angiotensin (Fig. 2.2).

Stimuli such as a reduction in renal perfusion pressure increase renin secretion from the juxtaglomerular cells surrounding the renal afferent arterioles as they enter glomeruli. Renin converts angiotensinogen (a circulating alpha globulin) into angiotensin I. Converting enzyme from the lung then converts this into angio-tensin II, an octapeptide which in turn stimulates aldosterone release (Fig. 2.3).

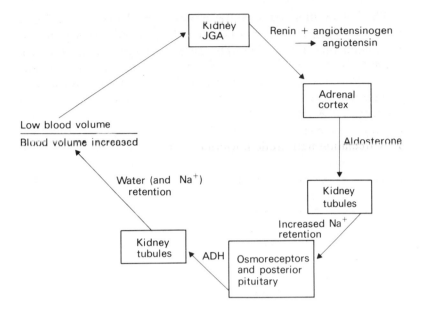

Fig. 2.2 Effects of aldosterone on sodium retention.

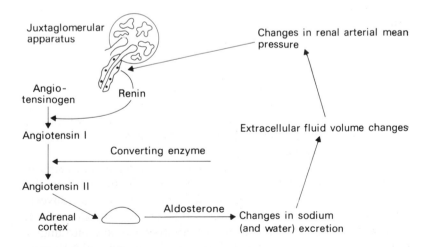

Fig. 2.3 The renin angiotensin system.

The role of this aldosterone secreting mechanism is probably mainly in defence of intravascular volume rather than primarily regulation of Na excretion. The site of action of aldosterone is probably in the cortical and medullary collecting ducts. It is relatively slow to act and concerned with fine regulation. Aldosterone secretion increases on rising from supine to the upright position and Na secretion is inhibited. However, this mechanism develops too rapidly for the increase in aldosterone to be totally responsible. Aldosterone secretion takes 10–30 minutes to exert any effect on Na excretion even if injected directly into the renal artery. This may represent the time required for increased enzyme secretion. Neither can this mechanism account for the regulation of Na excretion completely since if a large salt intake is given with a high dose of exogenous mineralocorticoid an *escape* phenomenon occurs and salt excretion eventually increases so that all the salt intake in excess of normal losses is in fact excreted. Before this mineralocorticoid escape occurs some ECF expansion may occur prior to the new steady state but oedema does not occur.

Third factor

This escape may occur because of a third factor (natriuretic hormone). In fact third factor is a series of different substances inhibiting tubular and collecting duct Na reabsorption as will be discussed below.

TRADITIONAL VIEW OF SODIUM AND CHLORIDE EXCRETION

Sodium is filtered in the glomerulus, a large amount appearing in filtrate. It is, however, transported out of the tubule either actively or passively following active chloride transport (see Chapter 1). The true distal tubule is capable of Na reabsorption independent of aldosterone whereas Na transport in the cortical collecting system is aldosterone dependent. Very large amounts of Na are filtered daily (26 000 mmol). If tubular reabsorption stays constant, a small variation in glomerular filtration rate produces a marked change in Na excretion. In fact, of course tubular reabsorption of Na varies with GFR but never completely compensates for changes in filtered load, hence the importance of GFR in affecting the amount of Na excreted. In the tubule most of the Na is reabsorbed with chloride but some is exchanged for hydrogen and potassium by tubular secretion (see Fig. 3.4).

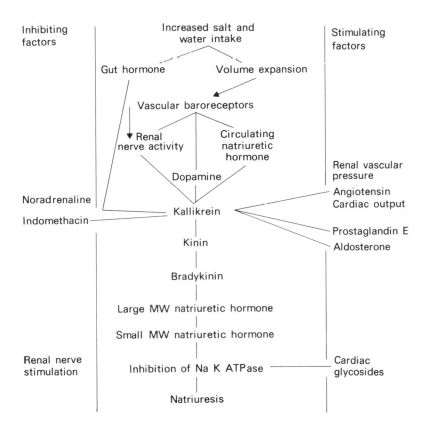

Fig. 2.4   Response to volume expansion with saline.

Fig. 2.4 illustrates the response to volume expansion with saline. There is a good correlation between the rate of Na excretion and urinary dopamine excretion. This dopamine is synthesised within the kidney and acts on specific dopamine receptors activating the kallikrein/kinin system. This system plays a key role in control of Na excretion and it is at this level that blood pressure and angiotensin exert their effects. Other factors act via prostaglandin E to increase kallikrein release. Noradrenaline has two effects: inhibition of the prostaglandin stimulation of kallikrein and a direct action on renal tubular cells to stimulate Na/K ATPase. Stimulation of the kallikrein kinin system by dopamine results in production of natriuretic hormone which inhibits renal Na/K ATPase to produce natriuresis (Fig. 2.5). Na/K ATPase is the common pathway then in Na excretion. Stimulation of this enzyme is the major Na retaining mechanism and inhibition results in Na excretion or natriuresis.

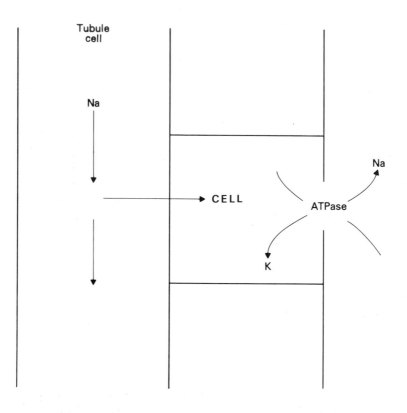

Fig. 2.5   Final common pathway in Na excretion.

OTHER FACTORS CONCERNED WITH SODIUM EXCRETION

Colloid osmotic pressure

Colloid osmotic pressure in peritubular capillaries surrounding the proximal tubule controls reabsorption of Na and water in this region. Proximal tubular Na reabsorption occurs in three stages.

1 Sodium ions diffuse passively from the tubular lumen into proximal tubular cells.

2 Sodium or chloride ions are pumped out of the cells into intercellular spaces between the cells producing local hypertonicity. Chloride or sodium and water follow passively to render isotonicity.

3 Isotonic fluid passes into peritubular capillaries and leaks back into the tubular lumen via tight junctions between tubular epithelial cells.

Na and water reabsorption in the proximal tubule is equal to the total volume of isotonic resorbate formed within the intercellular spaces minus the volume of that which diffuses back into the tubular lumen.

This suggests that the net proximal Na and water reabsorption is increased if peritubular capillary blood has a high colloid osmotic pressure. Infusion of crystalloid solutions will lower capillary colloid osmotic pressure and result in reduced reabsorption.

In congestive cardiac failure excess salt and water retention may result in oedema. This may be explained by an increase in peritubular plasma protein and hence colloid osmotic pressure again resulting in increased Na and water reabsorption.

Hydrostatic pressure

As in capillaries elsewhere the hydrostatic pressure difference across the peritubular capillary wall is an important factor in reabsorption. A high capillary hydrostatic pressure will reduce reabsorption.

Blood flow

If the peritubular blood flow rate is low this may allow earlier dilution of the peritubular capillary blood by resorbate, an earlier reduction of colloid osmotic pressure and reduced net salt and water reabsorption. A high rate of blood flow allows less time for reduction in colloid osmotic pressure but increased net Na and water reabsorption.

SODIUM REABSORPTION ALONG THE NEPHRON

Proximal tubule

1   Normally 60–70% of filtered Na is reabsorbed in this region.
2   All proximal reabsorption is isotonic.
3   The composition of tubular fluid changes along the tubule.
Active reabsorption of bicarbonate occurs early in the proximal tubule in excess of water reabsorption. This results in a reduction in bicarbonate concentration in tubular fluid and in exchange chloride concentration is increased.
4   Na reabsorption in this area may be active or passive (Na ions moving down a favourable electrical gradient generated by active or passive chloride diffusion). Much of the glucose and amino acid reabsorption is Na coupled.

Ascending limb of the loop of Henle

20–30% of filtered Na is reabsorbed here. The traditional view states that Na is actively pumped out of this segment to produce the hypertonic interstitium required for operation of the counter-current mechanism. More recent concepts suggest that it is chloride which is actively pumped out, facilitated by Na-K ATPase and Na then follows passively along a favourable concentration gradient.

Distal tubule

1   The early part of this segment is the true distal tubule.
2   The latter part is the beginning of the collecting duct in the cortex. In the true distal tubule active Na reabsorption takes place independently of aldosterone whereas Na reabsorption in the cortical collecting duct is aldosterone dependent.
3   5–10% of the filtered Na is reabsorbed in the distal tubule either

in association with the chloride or under the influence of aldosterone in exchange for potassium or hyrogen ion.

Collecting duct

Na reabsorption here is extremely variable depending on the action
of aldosterone and antidiuretic hormone and on the patient's Na
status. This area is extremely important in regulating Na balance
and urinary Na output. In salt depletion marked Na reabsorption
occurs but in salt overload no Na is reabsorbed and recent suggestions point to Na secretion in the collecting duct.

CHLORIDE BALANCE

This is very similar to Na balance.

Intake

Via the gastrointestinal tract 70–210 mmol of chloride are ingested
as sodium chloride or potassium chloride in food and drink daily.
The minimum daily requirement of chloride is 75 mmol. Chloride is
absorbed in the intestine with Na and potassium by an unknown
active process.

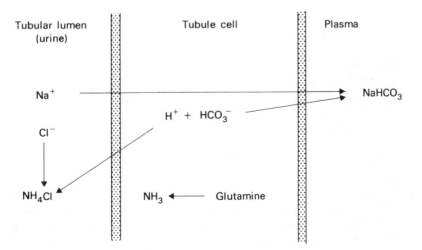

Fig. 2.6 Bicarbonate reabsorption in the tubule.

Output

Chloride is lost:

1   In the sweat with Na in a concentration of about 15 mmol l^{-1}.
2   In gastric juice 90–150 mmol l^{-1}.
3   In bile, pancreatic and intestinal fluids 50–100 mmol 1^{-1}.

In the renal tubule chloride excretion varies with the needs of the body for bicarbonate. Chloride is excreted with ammonium ions to eliminate hydrogen ion in exchange for Na (Fig. 2.6).

This occurs mainly in the proximal tubule. In the ascending limb of the loop of Henle, chloride is reabsorbed with Na (Fig. 1.9). Regulation of chloride is passively related to Na but inversely related to plasma bicarbonate. Aldosterone therefore indirectly influences chloride levels.

Chapter 3
Normal Potassium Balance

Potassium is of the soil and not the sea,
of the cell and not the sap.

W.O. FENN (1940)

Most of the potassium (K) within the human body is within the cells.
A 70 kg man contains 2900–3500 mmol of K.
Normal plasma K is 3.5–4.8 mmol l^{-1}.
Intracellular K is about 150 mmol l^{-1}.
Therefore only about 60 mmol of K (2% of the total body K) is
found in ECF. In effect therefore large changes may occur in total
body K without a significant effect on plasma K concentration.

EXCHANGEABLE K (K_e)

This is the pool of K within the body which comes into equilibrium
with the radioactive isotope ^{42}K within 24 hours. In humans virtually all K is exchangeable with two exceptions:
1   K in erythrocytes exchanges only slowly.
2   Some of the K in bone equilibrates only very slowly with ^{42}K.
  Exchangeable K in males is 42–48 mmol kg^{-1} body weight.
  Exchangeable K in females is 34–38 kg^{-1} body weight.
  Thus there is a significant difference between the sexes: the highest
value of total body K being in muscular males. In both sexes total
body K declines with age.
  K_e has been related to Na_e and to total body water. In health the
relationship Na_e/K_e is approximately 0.85 in males and 1.0 in
females. This relationship rises in illnesses such as sepsis, heart
failure and trauma where cell membrane function may be impaired,
to 1.5.
The following relationship has been demonstrated between Na_e, K_e and
total body water.
$$Na_e + K_e \text{ (mmol)} = 163.19 \text{ TBW(1)}-69.$$
$$r = 0.99 \ (P< 0.001).$$

43

Membrane polarisation

Despite the fact that a very small proportion of total body K is present in ECF it is regulation of plasma concentration which is very important for maintaining membrane polarisation.

Cells within the human body exist in a state of polarity. There is a resting potential difference of 50–90 mV between the inside and outside of the cell (the inside being negative to the outside). The magnitude of this potential is proportional to the ratio of the concentration of the most permeable ions on each side of the membrane. In the resting state K is the most permeable ion and therefore the difference in its concentration between the inside and the outside of the cell is the main determinant of the membrane potential. Na is much less permeable in the resting state than K and under normal circumstances does not leak into the cell. In excitable tissue an action potential results in passage of Na into the cell, the membrane potential then falls and depolarisation occurs. The magnitude of an action potential depends on the distribution of Na across the cell membrane. Following this event the sodium pump restores Na to its extracellular position and K equilibrium is restored.

MEASUREMENT OF POTASSIUM

Exchangeable potassium

This is measured using the radioactive isotope ^{42}K which equilibrates with 90% of total body K within 24 hours. ^{42}K is given intravenously or orally. When blood is collected for measurement of ^{42}K activity plasma should be separated from red cells within 2 hours of sampling.

Total body potassium

This requires a whole body counter to measure the emission of naturally occurring ^{40}K and is therefore of limited clinical application. However it has been recently demonstrated that there is a good correlation between total circulating blood cell K content and whole body K. Potassium concentration can be measured directly in erythrocytes, leucocytes and skeletal muscle cells.

Plasma potassium

This may be measured by:
1 Flame photometry.
2 Ion specific electrodes.
These methods have been discussed in Chapter 2 under measurement of plasma Na.

Interpretation and value of such measurements

A measurement of total body K as a prediction of K depletion or excess is very limited since the range of normal is wide and a 20% change is required before we can be assured of abnormal total body K. Serial changes in one individual are much more informative. These same restrictions also apply to exchangeable K. Many forms of illness lead to a catabolic state in which endogenous protein from muscle is broken down for energy releasing a large amount of K into plasma which is then excreted in the urine. Artifacts can occur during blood sampling. The same precautions should be taken as suggested for Na measurement. It is most important that haemolysis is avoided otherwise a spuriously high K may result by leakage from red blood cells. Samples should not therefore be shaken and plasma should always be separated within 2 hours of sampling. Refridgeration worsens hacmolysis. In the course of blood clotting K is released from cellular components of blood but in the normal patient this is without clinical significance. Some blood disorders in which leucocytes or platelets are abnormally fragile may result in a spuriously high K value. even severe muscle exercise may raise plasma K. As less than 3% of total body K is found in the ECF the relation between plasma K and total body K is tenuous. Total body K depletion can occur with a normal or raised plasma K. Although a low plasma K does indicate depletion this must be severe before the plasma level reflects the change in total body K. At least 10% of total body K (400 mmol) must be lost before there is any reflection in plasma K.

Factors which have an effect on membrane transport have a marked effect on plasma K whilst total body K remains unchanged.

These factors are:
1 Acid base state.
2 Diuretics.
3 Carbohydrate metabolism.

4 Hypoxia.
5 Digitalis.
Their effects are mediated by a change in ICF to ECF ratio.

It is unwise to treat an isolated abnormality of plasma K without consideration of the full clinical picture. In an acute disturbance it is the plasma concentration which is crucial regardless of the total body status since plasma concentration has the greatest effect on the membrane potential. In any event if an acute K disturbance exists or rapid replacement is contemplated continuous electrocardiographic (ECG) monitoring is invaluable to show minute by minute changes in transmembrane K gradient. Although strictly this constitutes an abnormal situation the changes in the ECG will be illustrated here as they show the importance of the K level on membrane electrophysiology.

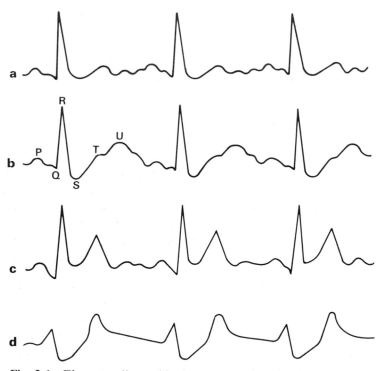

Fig. 3.1 Electrocardiographic changes at various levels of plasma potassium. a, normal ECG; b, hypokalaemia; c, hyperkalaemia; d, severe hyperkalaemia.

When plasma K is less than 3.0 mmol l^{-1} the T wave becomes broader and flatter and the U wave may fuse with the T wave (Fig. 3.1b). As plasma K rises the QRS widens the tall peaked T waves appear (Fig. 3.1c). The P wave then becomes less prominent and may disappear (Fig. 3.1d). The ECG then takes on the appearance of a sine wave.

POTASSIUM BALANCE

Intake

The daily K intake is between 50–100 mmol varying widely with dietary food and fluid habits. It is almost impossible that a diet containing sufficient energy will be deficient in K but as patients are prepared for surgery by starvation then K intake immediately falls and a situation of negative K balance occurs. Potassium intake normally greatly exceeds requirements and whereas most of the Na in the diet is in the form of added salt, K is present in all living cells and therefore fruit, vegetables and meat contain 100 times as much K as Na so that K free diets are totally impractical.

Output

Obligatory losses:
1 Skin and normal stools: 15–20 mmol daily.
2 Urine: 10–20 mmol daily.
Potassium cannot be so efficiently conserved by the kidney as can Na although there is a large reserve for the excretion of K. Thus a minimum of 40 mmol K are required to cover basal daily losses.

Postoperative situation

After uneventful surgery 50–100 mmol K may be lost in the urine in the first 48 hours. If in addition the surgery is severe or associated with postoperative complications such as sepsis, wound breakdown or prolonged ileus this K loss continues throughout the period of catabolism in conjunction with muscle breakdown and negative nitrogen balance. Intake is likely to be reduced as K is often withheld in the immediate postoperative period. Therefore considerable deficits of K can occur within a few days of an operation if no K is administered and it must be remembered that this may not be reflected in a low plasma K. Evaluation of K balance may be helped by measurement of 24 hour urinary K losses. If the loss is less than 60% of the K intake then a total body K deficit can be presumed to exist. It should be remembered that very significant losses of K can occur from the gastrointestinal tract especially if nasogastric suction or prolonged diarrhoea are problems. This is discussed further in Chapter 7. Intravenous administration of K salts results in rapid equilibration. If the cardiac output is normal 95% equilibrium occurs in a single transit through the circulation.

Regulation of potassium balance under normal circumstances

In man mechanisms to prevent K overload are much more highly developed than those to prevent K loss and respond directly to changes in plasma K. Since it determines membrane polarisation it is the plasma K concentration that requires precise regulation by one of two mechanisms:

1   Changes in K distribution across the cell membrane.
2   Renal excretion.

Renal excretion is responsible for long term regulation of K balance whereas changes in distribution across the cell membrane account for acute alterations in plasma K. Decreased K intake or excessive loss is 'buffered' by release of K from cells into ECF.

Mechanisms for acute redistribution of potassium

1   Autonomic nervous system.
2   Pancreatic hormones.
3   Acid base status.

Autonomic nervous system: adrenaline

1   Adrenaline increases plasma K by an alpha adrenergic effect.
2   Following this adrenaline produces a sustained decrease in plasma K by a beta adrenergic effect which is independent of insulin. This effect can be blocked by beta 2 or nonselective beta adrenergic blockade but not by beta 1 blockade. One of the ganglion blocking drugs currently used for inducing hypotension has

been shown to reduce plasma K for the period of intraoperative hypotension.

Pancreatic hormones

INSULIN

An increase in plasma K which is well within the normal physiological range will stimulate insulin release resulting in uptake of glucose and K into cells from ECF (Fig. 3.2)

GLUCAGON

An increase in plasma K also stimulates release of glucagon which raises plasma glucose.

The net effect of these two hormones is uptake of K into cells with minimal effect on blood glucose. This K uptake into cells with glucose facilitated by insulin is one of the most rapid means of reducing a high plasma K and is used therapeutically.

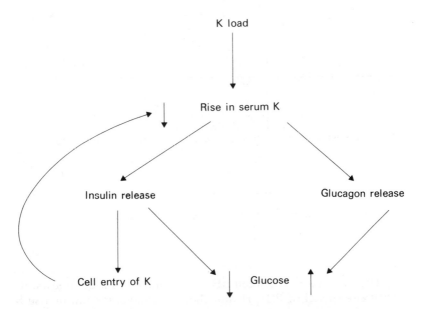

Fig. 3.2 Pancreatic hormones in acute redistribution of potassium.

The effectiveness of these hormones has been demonstrated in pancreatectomised dogs given a K load. Survival time is dramatically reduced unless the K load is accompanied by insulin and glucagon. Conversely in diabetics insulin induced hypoglycaemia may be associated with dangerous hypokalaemia.

Acid base status

Intracellular pH has an important effect on K ion activity. An intracellular alkalosis (low hydrogen (H) ion concentration) promotes influx of K into the cell to restore electrical neutrality. Intracellular acidosis (high H ion concentration) conversely inhibits K influx into cells and favours movement of K out into ECF.

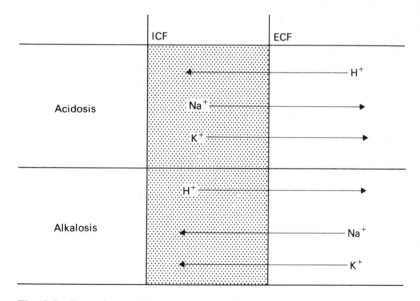

Fig. 3.3 Potassium exchange in acute disturbances of pH.

The relationship between pH and K in plasma is as follows: for each rise or fall of 0.1 pH unit there is an average fall or rise in plasma K of 0.63 mmol l^{-1}.

Renal regulation of potassium balance

There is a good correlation between total body K content and K excretion by the kidney but the correlation between plasma K and urinary excretion is poor. The kidney has a large excretory reserve for K.

There are no regulatory mechanisms controlling K intake, absorption or proximal renal tubular absorption. 85–90% of filtered K is reabsorbed in the proximal renal tubule and further reabsorption takes place in the loop of Henle. Therefore the glomerular load of K is all reabsorbed by this time and K excretion is entirely due to distal tubular mechanisms. In the absence of renal failure the glomerular filtration rate (GFR) normally has little effect on K excretion. The only exceptions to this are in the following abnormal circumstances:

1 Osmotic diuresis
2 Massive ECF volume expansion
3 Administration of frusemide.

In these cases delivery of a larger than normal K load to the distal renal tubule contributes to urinary excretion of K.

Tubular fluid to plasma K concentration ratios increase from 0.2–5.0 along the distal tubule. The collecting ducts contribute little to K excretion. Net reabsorption of K is only seen after severe dietary restriction. There is evidence of an active reabsorption mechanism which is inhibited by ouabain. Net excretion can be increased by a diet rich in K.

Distal tubular regulatory mechanisms

The main factors influencing K excretion are:

1 Aldosterone.
2 Acid base status.
3 Na/K ATPase activity.
4 Flow rate through the distal tubule.

ALDOSTERONE

Aldosterone is the most potent of the naturally occurring mineralocorticoid hormones and is concerned in the regulation of Na and K balance. A K load increases aldosterone production and K depletion diminishes it. This effect is probably quite independent of changes in the volumes of body fluids and the renin angiotensin system. The effect of aldosterone is to conserve Na and promote excretion of K (see also Chapter 2). An increase in plasma K of less than 0.5 mmol l^{-1} will increase aldosterone secretion whilst a pre-existing high K intake will magnify the response to an acute K load. Aldosterone therefore is a powerful controller of ECF K concentration such that a sevenfold rise in K load only increases plasma K by 2–2.5%.

Mechanism of action of aldosterone. The distal tubular lumen becomes progressively more electronegative as Na is actively reabsorbed. This favours passive movement of K into the lumen of the tubule to restore electrical neutrality. In addition to this passive movement of K into the tubular lumen K is also actively secreted into the tubular lumen (Fig. 3.4). This effect is maximal in the late distal tubule.

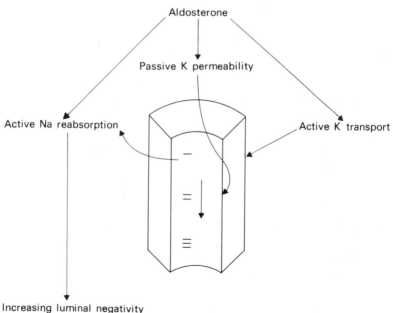

Fig. 3.4   Action of aldosterone on the distal renal tubule.

Aldosterone enhances both these effects:

1 It increases passive K permeability

2 It increases the active K entry from peritubular fluid into the distal tubular cells. If excess aldosterone activity is present K depletion and hypokalaemia may occur. Then Na retention occurs and Na ions partly replace the the intracellular K deficit.

ACID BASE STATUS

In the presence of an alkalosis K secretion is increased and in acidosis it is decreased. Within the distal tubule both H ions and K ions compete for excretion in exchange for Na reabsorption.

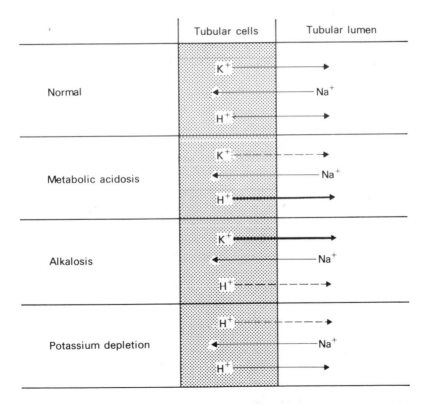

Fig. 3.5 Potassium flux in the distal tubule in acid base disturbance.

Metabolic alkalosis. When a metabolic alkalosis exists with a deficit of H ions intracellular K increases in all body cells including those in the distal tubule. The rate of K excretion is enhanced resulting in total body K depletion. This depletion will result in a fall in intracellular K. Therefore the tubule exchanges Na for K ions in order to conserve H ions. At a later stage K secretion will diminish and more H ions will be excreted. This results in paradoxical aciduria in alkalosis with K depletion.

Metabolic acidosis. In metabolic acidosis there is an increase in H ion excretion and the rate of K excretion is markedly diminished. These changes are illustrated in Fig. 3.5. Intracellular K concentrations are directly related to the rate of distal tubular K excretion. Changes in peritubular K uptake can partly explain the effects of a change in acid base state. A high K concentration therefore increases the efflux of K from cells into the tubular lumen and determines the rate of net secretion of K. Conversely a low K concentration reduces the efflux of this ion from cells into the tubular lumen. It is at this stage that an alkalosis exists with a paradoxical acid urine as the kidney has no alternative but to excrete H ions in exchange for Na. In this way tubular cells are simply behaving in the same way as the cells in the rest of the body. Diminished Na intake is associated with reduced K excretion by a mechanism which is not fully elucidated.

Bicarbonate (HCO_3). This ion may be taken as an index of H ion secretion (Fig. 3.6). Sodium is reabsorbed into the blood in exchange for H ions which arise from carbonic acid (facilitated by carbonic anhydrase). Bicarbonate ions for reabsorption with Na ions are formed from carbon dioxide (CO_2). In K depletion plasma HCO_3 is a quantitative measurement of the depletion. Plasma HCO_3 is raised due to accumulation of H ions within the K depleted cell. In metabolic alkalosis H ions secretion may be augmented due to the increased HCO_3 load delivered to the distal tubule. Hence as discussed above both H and K secretion are greater than normal.
In metabolic acidosis there is a reduction in the filtered HCO_3 load. Only small amounts of HCO_3 reach the distal tubule most being reabsorbed in the proximal tubule and loop of Henle. Less is therefore available to permit H ion excretion so that H and K excretion are both reduced.

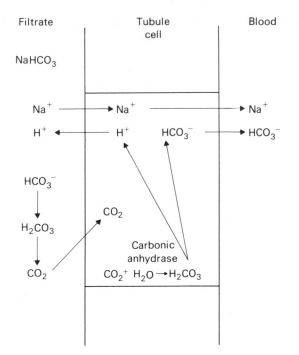

Fig. 3.6   Reabsorption of bicarbonate by the renal tubules.

SODIUM POTASSIUM ADENOSINE TRIPHOSPHATASE

The activity of this enzyme is induced by K loading and is entirely independent of aldosterone. When the level of ATPase is raised isolated perfused kidneys can excrete up to three times the amount of K filtered at the glomerulus. This mechanism is important in maintaining K excretion per nephron as renal function is reduced.

FLOW RATE IN THE DISTAL TUBULE

In the distal renal tubule the K gradient across the wall is *independent* of the tubular flow rate. Therefore a high rate of flow results in an increase in total K excretion and a low flow rate in a reduced K excretion.

Reduction in tubular flow. In a situation of Na or water depletion tubular flow will be reduced and in addition proximal tubular reabsorption of Na will be more complete. Referring to Fig. 3.4 there is a reduced gradient of electronegativity down the distal tubule and less passive transport of K into the lumen. Aldosterone has little effect in these circumstances. If however Na intake is high aldosterone will promote K excretion because there is more Na in the urine.

SUMMARY OF RESPONSES TO A RISE IN POTASSIUM INTAKE AND PLASMA CONCENTRATION

Ingestion of a high K load results in the following:
1 Stimulation of insulin and glucagon secretion.
2 Stimulation of aldosterone production.
3 Stimulation of Na/K ATPase in the renal medulla.

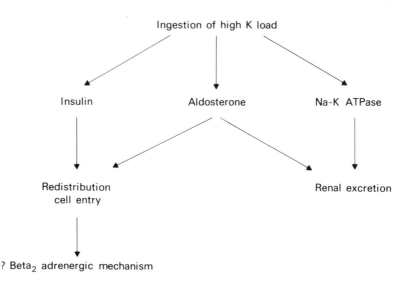

Fig. 3.7 Factors opposing hyperkalaemia after an acute potassium load.

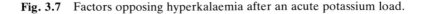

Following a high oral K intake the K content of the small bowel lumen approaches plasma concentration rapidly and passive absorption occurs across the mucosa into ECF. However ECF constitutes only a small percentage of the total body K pool so that unless ECF K is to reach a high level mechanisms must come into play rapidly to reduce this level.

If K is administered intravenously (i.v.) a more rapid rise in ECF K occurs since the stage of absorption across the mucosa is eliminated. This is why rapid i.v. administration of K may be particularly dangerous. In situations of chronically high K intake the efficiency of these mechanisms to limit the rise in plasma K is increased.

Sudden changes in K intake are rare however in humans. New Guineans migrating from a region of high to low K intake have developed hypokalaemic muscle paralysis within the first two months of the change. It seems then that there is considerable delay in modification of K excretion.

In any assessment of K balance it is important to remember that decreased K intake (effectively starvation) or an increased loss can to some extent be buffered by release of K from cells. Likewise increased K uptake by cells limits an acute rise in plasma K provided acid base regulation is normal, there is no lack of insulin nor is excess catabolism present.

Chapter 4
Normal Calcium, Phosphate and Magnesium Metabolism

I'll grind these bones to make my bread . . . .

Jack and the Beanstalk

Calcium (Ca), phosphate (PO₄) and magnesium (Mg) are all essential for normal function in man. Transport and distribution of these three ions are often closely associated although their intra and extracellular concentrations are independently determined. Significant abnormalities may be present without any alteration from normal plasma concentration of Ca, PO₄ or Mg. This is especially the case in abnormal acid base states, chronic renal or gastrointestinal disease or with the ever increasing problem of drug induced enzyme induction. Similarly, an abnormal plasma level may be present without disturbance in total metabolism, for example rapid uptake of PO₄ into cells occurs when insulin stimulates glucose uptake resulting in a lowering of plasma PO₄ level.

CALCIUM

Ca is the fifth most abundant element in the human body. Most of the Ca within the body is found in the skeleton. Ca is required for the following:
1   Calcification of bones and teeth.
2   Regulation of metabolism in all cells and excitability of nerve cells.
3   Cardiac conduction.
4   Blood clotting.
In an average 70 kg man, Ca constitutes about 2% of the total body weight and amounts to 32 500 mmol.
   99% of total body Ca is found within bone (32 125 mmol).
   0.5% is found in teeth (175 mmol).

0.5% is found in soft tissues.

Small amounts are found in plasma (8 mmol) where almost half is bound to albumin so that hypoalbuminaemia produces a low plasma Ca level with no disturbance in total body Ca or turnover of Ca.

Normal plasma Ca is 2.2–2.6 mmol l^{-1}.

Normal urine Ca is 2.5–7.5 mmol daily.

Table 4.1 Constitutents of plasma Ca.

	Plasma concentration (mmol l^{-1})
Free Ca	1.18
Albumin bound Ca	1.14
Calcium phosphate (CaHPO$_4$)	0.04
Calcium citrate	0.04
Unidentified	0.08
	2.48

It is important to sample blood for Ca measurement without use of a tourniquet because this encourages fluid loss from the vein and hence a spuriously high plasma protein concentration. It is quite possible to have a considerable abnormality in total body Ca with a normal plasma level.

Methods of measurement of plasma calcium

1 Atomic absorption spectroscopy.

2 Chemical methods.

Most laboratories analyse Ca in an autoanalyser, for example an SMA. One such method is to use an indicator, orthocresol-phthalein. This indicator binds Ca at the correct pH. The degree of binding is proportional to the plasma Ca concentration and results in a colour change.

3 Ion selective electrodes. Only ionised Ca is biologically active. It is this component which is measured by these electrodes. However

this forms only half of total plasma Ca since almost half the Ca in plasma is protein bound.

Clinicians usually have to rely on measurements of total plasma Ca.

Correction of plasma calcium

It is possible to apply correction factors to take abnormal plasma proteins into account. Most of these corrections use the plasma albumin as their basis. A commonly used correction factor is as follows:

For every 1 g l^{-1} by which the plasma albumin exceeds or is lower than 40 g l^{-1} subtract or add 0.02 mmol l^{-1} to the measured plasma Ca. It is important to remember that the ionised portion of Ca is also affected by venous stasis and pH of blood. The total Ca therefore is corrected to an arbitrary normal plasma albumin and although inaccuracy may occur, for clinical purposes in a stable patient this correction prevents the clinician diagnosing hypocalcaemia in a hypoalbuminaemic patient or hypercalcaemia in a sample taken with excessive venous stasis.

Many chemical pathologists condemn such corrections pointing out that these formulae have been worked out over a limited range of plasma protein concentrations and therefore may not apply in extremes such as found in the intensive care unit. Different laboratory methods in the presence of an unknown acid base state can make blind reporting of corrected Ca hazardous and the best approach may be to record a straight measured plasma Ca pointing out any abnormality in plasma proteins.

Physiological importance of calcium

Bone

99% of total body Ca is found in bone as hydroxyapatite. This is largely found as the supporting structure of bone but small amounts of Ca in equilibrium with this large fixed amount are exchangeable with ECF and soft tissue Ca. Hence an enormous reservoir of Ca exists which through this small exchangeable pool can readily compensate for a fall in plasma Ca.

Cell membrane function

Ca is concerned with the following membrane functions:
1 Integrity.
2 Permeability.
3 Adhesiveness.
4 Intercellular connections.

Coupling of electrical or chemical excitation to intracellular contractile or secretory events

1 Specific Ca binding sites have been postulated on cell membranes which alter the permeability to Na and hence the excitability of the cell.
2 Ca is necessary for synaptic release of acetylcholine following an action potential in the nerve which then leads to muscle contraction.
3 Ca mediates the insulin secretion response to hyperglycaemia.
4 Close regulation of the plasma Ca concentration is necessary for normal muscle activity. A reduction in ionised Ca produces tetany whereas hypercalcemia produces muscle weakness and paralysis. For initiation of muscle contraction, Ca moves from its binding site on the sarcoplasmic reticulum, via an ATP dependent mechanism to actomyosin. Muscle contraction occurs which is terminated when Ca ions are released. It is well known from experiments in animal physiology that if Ca is absent from fluid perfusing the isolated heart it will stop beating. Addition of Ca restarts the heart. There is a significant correlation between low cardiac output and lowered ionised Ca levels.

Blood coagulation

Ca is important at several stages in the coagulation cascade.

Complement activation

This process proceeds in a similar cascade fashion to coagulation and Ca is again involved in this complex pathway.

Calmodulin

Calmodulin is a Ca binding protein which has been intensively studied over the last 10 years. When intracellular Ca levels rise following stimulation of the cell calmodulin binds Ca ions and the complex reacts with receptor protein. In smooth muscle calmodulin couples excitation and contraction. Calmodulin also stimulates efflux of Ca ions from the cell and hence promotes muscle relaxation by stimulating the Ca pump and in nerve cells it promotes phosphorylation of proteins.

Normal calcium turnover

Dietary sources of Ca are plentiful. It is found abundantly in milk, cheese and eggs. Minimum requirements are of the order of 10 mmol daily.

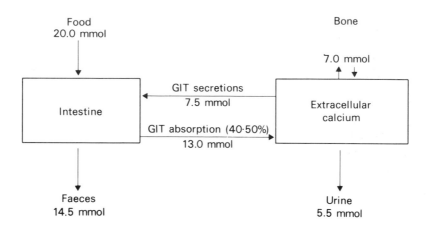

Fig. 4.1 Average daily calcium turnover for a 70 kg man. Ca MW = 40.08. GIT = gastrointestinal tract.

40–50% of dietary (and gastrointestinal secretion) Ca is absorbed in the small intestine. In extremes of intake this may range from 20 to 80%.

1 Active transport of Ca occurs in the duodenum, where Ca is absorbed against an electrochemical gradient. The active mechan-

ism is located within the mucosal cells. Subsequent absorption into the blood may be passive.

2 Passive absorption of Ca also occurs. The amount of absorption of Ca depends on the body *requirements*, not on Ca supply. Therefore absorption is increased during active growth periods in early life and during pregnancy and lactation. At a given steady growth rate on a low Ca diet, a greater proportion of the Ca intake will be absorbed; the amount depending on the amount of Ca intake and the level within the small intestine.

3 Ca secretion. This occurs in the small intestine relatively independently of the intake or growth rate and is therefore much less variable than absorption.

Ca intake varies widely with a mean of about 20 mmol from food. Faecal losses amount to about 14.5 mmol and urinary losses to about 5.5 mmol daily. Dietary intake of Ca has little effect on renal losses.

Factors affecting gastrointestinal absorption of calcium

Absorption is decreased by phosphates and oxalates as these form insoluble salts with Ca. Absorption is increased by the following factors:

1 Vitamin D.
2 Parathyroid hormone (PTH).
3 Growth hormone.
4 Corticosteroids.
5 Lactose.

Vitamin D

It is well known that vitamin D deficiency produces rickets in children and osteomalacia in adults. In animals a response to vitamin D administration is delayed for some hours, presumably whilst some vitamin D is converted into the active form (see below). The precise action of vitamin D in the intestine is not known but it may involve an increased production of Ca binding protein which is known to be raised during periods of active growth and in conditions of low Ca intake. In addition vitamin D enhances the activity of Ca activated ATPase in the intestinal mucosa and this may be the mediator of vitamin D induced Ca transport.

PTH

In man hypocalcaemia stimulates PTH to increase the proportion of Ca intake which is absorbed BUT a decrease in the concentration of plasma Ca would normally improve passive Ca absorption because the gradient between intestinal lumen and plasma is more favourable.

Growth hormone

In growth hormone deficiency states Ca absorption is depressed.

Corticosteroid

Glucocorticoids depress the stimulatory effect of vitamin D on intestinal Ca absorption.

Lactose

Lactose increases intestinal absorption of Ca.

Approximately 13 mmol Ca daily are absorbed from the intestine into ECF from which there is interchange with Ca within bone during deposition or reabsorption (7 mmol daily) and loss of Ca into gastrointestinal secretions (7.5 mmol daily). Although adequate absorption of Ca and PO_4 from the gut is essential for mineralisation of bone the ECF and Ca content and hence plasma concentration is minimally affected by dietary intake or absorption being closely regulated by hormonal mechanisms. Regulation of Ca metabolism is extremely complex and aimed at maintaining intracellular ionised Ca at a concentration of about 10^{-7} M. It is this concentration which is critically important for muscle activity, endocrine secretion and nervous system function and in the long term depends on maintenance of ECF Ca by hormonal activity.

Regulation of plasma calcium level

This hinges around three hormones: vitamin D, PTH and calcitonin. Other factors are of lesser importance.

Vitamin D

Historically vitamin D describes that constituent of the diet that prevents rickets. Cholecalciferol (D_3) occurs naturally and is made in the skin by the action of sunlight (ultraviolet) on the provitamin. Ergocalciferol (D_2) is present in fish liver and is derived from a provitamin found in some plants and fungi. Vitamin D_3 itself however is almost inactive.

There have been enormous developments in the last 10 years in recognising the metabolites of vitamin D. Cholecalciferol is hydroxylated in the liver and perhaps other organs to produce 25 hydroxycholecalciferol (25 (OH) D_3.) Many enzyme inducing drugs may increase this microsomal process so that more polar, less active derivatives are produced that are excreted in the bowel. 25 (OH) D_3 however is still relatively inactive although it is the major circulating form of the vitamin. It is transported on a specific gamma globulin binding protein to the kidney, where further hydroxylation occurs to produce several metabolites the most important of which are:

1   1,25 dihydroxycholecalciferol ($1,25(OH)_2D_3$).
2   24,25 dihydroxycholecalciferol ($24,25(OH)_2D_3$).

This second hydroxylation is crucial and occurs only in the kidney.

$1,25(OH)_2D_3$

This is an extremely active metabolite with the following actions:
1   It stimulates the absorption of Ca and PO_4 from the gut.
2   It stimulates Ca and PO_4 resorption from bone.
3   It stimulates the reabsorption of Ca and PO_4 from renal tubules.

The overall effect $1,25(OH)_2D_3$ is maintenance of Ca and PO_4 concentration in ECF and promotion of normal bone calcification. The healing action of vitamin D in rickets seems to be entirely due to its action in raising plasma Ca and PO_4 levels.

$1,25(OH)_2D_3$ levels are high in conditions of increased demand such as rapid growth, pregnancy and lactation, and may be regulated by the pituitary. Low concentrations of plasma Ca or PO_4 increase circulating $1,25(OH)_2D_3$ via a feedback loop.

$24,25(OH)_2D_3$ is definitely a less active metabolite which may promote normal formation and mineralisation of bone or represent simply a diversionary pathway used when there is no increase in Ca requirement. It has only recently become clear that the pituitary is of major importance in regulating secretion of $1,25(OH)_2D_3$. Both growth hormone and prolactin and perhaps high concentrations of oestrogen enhance the production of $1,25(OH)_2D_3$ in mammals. $1,25(OH)_2D_3$ may suppress PTH activity.

Parathormone

PTH only evolved with land mammals when phosphate intake became important. The phosphaturic effect of PTH allowed survival on land with a high PO_4 diet. PTH is a polypeptide (MW 9500) consisting of a single chain of amino acids. It has long been held that when plasma levels of Ca, Mg and other divalent ions fell secretion of this hormone occurs from the chief cells of the parathyroid glands. Plasma levels of Ca and PO_4 are then restored towards normal by an an action on the bone and kidneys.

BONE

Within bone both osteoblastic and osteoclastic activity are stimulated resulting in release of Ca and PO_4 into ECF and therefore increasing plasma levels. This process involves $1,25(OH)_2D_3$.

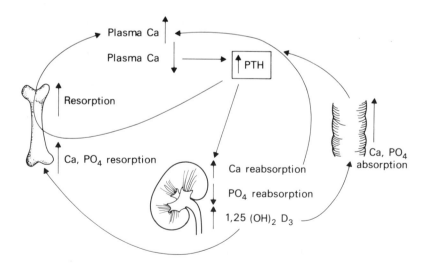

Fig. 4.2 The relation between parathormone, calcium and vitamin D.

KIDNEY

PTH increases renal tubular reabsorption of Ca and Mg and reduces that of PO_4.

The postulated mechanism for regulation of plasma Ca therefore is that hypocalcaemia stimulates PTH production which increases $1,25(OH)_2D_3$, mobilises Ca and PO_4 from bone, increases gastrointestinal absorption of Ca and PO_4 and permits PO_4 loss with Ca retention by the kidney. As the plasma Ca is restored $1,25(OH)_2D_3$ levels return to normal and $24,25(OH)_2D_3$ levels increase. Until recently it was thought that PTH was essential for regulation of vitamin D metabolism but it now appears that increased levels of $1,25(OH)_2D_3$ do not depend primarily on variation of PTH secretion although considerable controversy still exists regarding the regulation of Ca metabolism by vitamin D and PTH.

Calcitonin

This hormone is a 32 amino acid polypeptide from the parafollicular (C) cells of the thyroid which is released when ECF Ca levels rise. Its actions reduce plasma Ca.

ACTIONS OF CALCITONIN

1 Inhibition of bone resorption. This is the main effect of calcitonin.
2 Renal excretion of Ca and PO_4 are increased whereas that of Mg is decreased.
3 Gastrointestinal absorption of Ca and PO_4 may also be reduced.
   Inhibition of skeletal resorption results in a fall in urine hydroxyproline. If calcitonin is injected into *normal* adults there is little or no change in plasma Ca. This is because under normal circumstances the Ca efflux from bone forms only a small percentage of the net movement of Ca into plasma. Calcitonin will produce hypocalcaemia however during periods of active growth or in Paget's disease where bone turnover is enhanced. There is normally marked diurnal variation in plasma levels of calcitonin.

FACTORS WHICH STIMULATE CALCITONIN SECRETION

1 Hypercalcaemia.

2 Glucagon.
3 Pentagastrin.
4 Cholecystokinin.
5 Catecholamines.
6 Alcohol.
7 Presence of food in stomach.
8 Oral contraceptive pill.
9 Pregnancy.

Under normal physiological conditions calcitonin is of little importance. It does have a role in regulating plasma Ca but may be more important for ensuring skeletal homeostasis and it may be that lack of calcitonin is an important factor in the rapid bone loss which occurs in women after the menopause. There is a striking sex difference in circulating plasma calcitonin with a relative deficiency in women. Calcitonin secretion in young adults is increased by

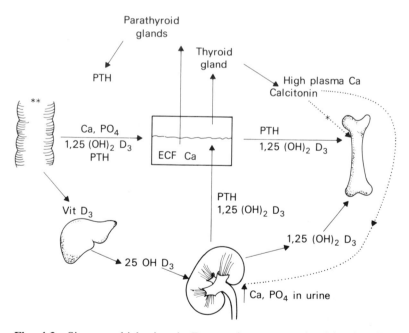

Fig. 4.3 Sites at which vitamin D, parathormone and calcitonin affect plasma calcium concentration. *1,25(OH)₂ D₃ may also stimulate deposition of Ca, PO₄ in bone. **Calcitonin may reduce gastrointestinal absorption of calcium and phosphate.

oestrogens and recent studies of the effects of oestrogen in post-menopausal women show a sharp increase in plasma calcitonin. Oestrogens prevent postmenopausal bone loss and this effect could be mediated at least in part by control of calcitonin secretion.

THYROXIN AND TRIIODOTHYRONIN

These hormones increase bone Ca and PO_4 turnover. Hyper-calcaemia may be seen in thyrotoxicosis.

GROWTH HORMONE

In addition to its effect on intestinal absorption growth hormone also induces retention of Ca in bone.

GLUCAGON

Glucagon may produce a fall in plasma Ca by either direct suppression of bone resorption or by release of calcitonin. Glucagon release may be one cause of hypocalcaemia in pancreatitis.

GLUCOCORTICOIDS

It is well known that chronic steroid therapy leads to osteoporosis. In addition to their effect on the gastrointestinal tract, glucocorticoids inhibit bone resorption and promote Ca and PO_4 excretion in the urine.

Summary of interactions of calcium regulating hormones (Fig. 4.3)

1 The gastrointestinal tract, kidney and bone control Ca homeostasis.
2 $1,25(OH)_2D_3$ is the main regulator of Ca and PO_4 absorption from the gut and is important mainly for providing Ca and PO_4 for the foetus and growing child. Its destructive effect on bone is normally prevented by calcitonin since levels of both these hormones are increased in growth, pregnancy and lactation. Therefore the presence of calcitonin is necessary for the normal action of $1,25(OH)_2D_3$.
3 PTH controls Ca excretion by the kidney. It promotes excretion of PO_4 by the kidney whilst enhancing tubular reabsorption of Ca.

Its less important action is on the gut and is indirect enhancing Ca and PO_4 absorption by an increase in $1,25(OH)_2D_3$ production. Direct action of PTH on bone is probably not important in maintaining plasma Ca.

4 Calcitonin controls the rate of skeletal resorption by interaction with $1,25(OH)_2D_3$.

Calcium and the kidney

Renal handling of Ca is similar to that for Mg (see below) except that both free and some unionised complexes of Ca are filtered at the glomerulus and there is no doubt that PTH specifically stimulates resorption of Ca. A reciprocal relationship exists between Ca and PO_4 excretion. Ca and Mg are maximally excreted in the morning, PO_4 in the afternoon.

In addition to direct regulation of Ca, Mg and PO_4 by hormones and cellular transport mechanisms there is indirect regulation due to interaction with other ions. For example in metabolic alkalosis (low hydrogen (H) ion concentration) there is increased muscular excitability as in tetany due to hypocalcaemia. This is only partly due to an alteration in the relationship between free and bound Ca and effects of H ion concentration on Ca binding at nerve membranes may also be important. In addition reciprocal movement of Ca and H ions can be observed in mitochondrial transport.

It must be stressed that it is the free ionised Ca which is taking part in essential physiological mechanisms but that this constitutes only about 50% of the total plasma Ca. The extent of Ca binding by plasma proteins is in direct proportion to the plasma albumin level, therefore it is essential for this to be measured at the same time as the Ca measurement is undertaken.

PHOSPHATE

Phosphorus constitutes 1% of the total body weight and is the sixth most abundant element in the body. Total body phosphorus content is 22 600 mmol. Within the body phosporus is in the form of phosphate ion, PO_4, and it is this form which is measured in the plasma.

Table 4.2   Distribution of phosphorus in a 70 kg adult man.

	%	mmol
Bone	85.0	19 200
Teeth	0.4	98
Soft tissue	14.3	3230
Extravascular fluid	0.03	7
Blood		
plasma	0.02	4
erythrocytes	0.3	61

Normal plasma PO_4 concentration is 0.8–1.35 mmol l^{-1}.

Normal urine PO_4 excretion is 4.0–17 mmol l^{-1}.

As with Ca significant derangement can occur without a significant abnormality in plasma PO_4 level. This is especially so in the following circumstances:

1   Acid base disturbances.

2   Chronic renal and gastrointestinal disease.

3   Drug induced abnormalities of vitamin D metabolism.

Equally either high or low plasma PO_4 levels may occur without significant disturbances of total body PO_4 content or turnover for example during haemoconcentration or dilution, during haemolysis and during hydrolysis of PO_4 containing compounds.

Measurement of plasma PO_4 levels

Blood should be sampled from a fasting patient without use of a tourniquet and the laboratory should be informed if a glucose infusion is in progress as this lowers plasma PO_4 owing to uptake of PO_4 into the cells with glucose under the influence of insulin.

Measurement of plasma PO_4 utilises a chemical method first described by Fisk and Subbarow. It involves the reduction of phosphomolybdate to molybdenum when a colour change takes place proportional to the PO_4 concentration. PO_4 may be routinely measured in an autoanalyser. It is present in several forms within plasma.

Table 4.3 Plasma Po₄ concentration (mmol l⁻¹).

Free HPO_4^{--}	0.5
Free $H_2PO_4^{-}$	0.11
Protein bound	0.14
Na_2HPO_4	0.33
$CaHPO_4$	0.04
$MgHPO_4$	0.03

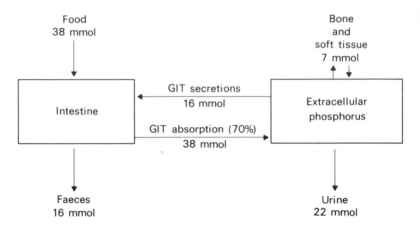

Fig. 4.4 Daily turnover of phosphorus. MW = 30.98.

Daily turnover of phosphorus

Dietary PO₄ is in good supply. Minimum daily requirements are 25 mmol. The average daily adult intake is about 40 mmol. In the adult only enough PO₄ is retained to compensate for normal losses via the urine and faeces but in children during growth or in pregnancy and lactation requirements are increased with net PO₄ retention. Almost three quarters of dietary PO₄ is absorbed, faecal losses amount to 14–16 mmol daily. Low dietary intake of PO₄ reduces plasma PO₄ in normal people and high intake results in increased urinary excretion. Plasma PO₄ levels may be markedly reduced during insulin facilitated uptake of glucose into cells. Once absorbed into ECF some 7 mmol PO_4 interchanges daily with bone PO_4. 16 mmol daily appears in gastrointestinal tract secretion and 22–26 mmol is excreted in the urine.

Physiological importance of PO_4

85% of PO_4 is located in bone and 15% in soft tissues within cells as organic phosphorus compounds.

Intracellular phosphate

Intracellular phosphate occurs in the following forms:
1   Adenosine triphosphate (ATP). This nucleotide is a labile high energy PO_4 compound which is the final common energy providing compound for many reactions such as muscle contraction, hormone secretion and active transport of substances across cell membranes.
2   Nucleic acid.
3   Phospholipids.
4   Phosphoproteins.
Many of these compounds are important in maintaining the structure and function of cell membranes.

Buffer systems

Phosphate compounds exist in acidic or basic salts ($H_2PO_4^-$, HPO_4^{--}) and hence they form buffer systems in urine and cells.

Hypophosphataemia

Hypophosphataemia is now becoming increasingly recognised during parenteral nutrition when high concentrations of glucose containing solutions cause glucose and phosphate to enter the cells under the influence of insulin. Plasma PO_4 is an important determinant of red blood cell 2,3 diphosphoglycerate (2,3 DPG) which in turn determines the position of the oxygen dissociation curve. A reduction in 2,3 DPG results in a left shift of the oxygen dissociation curve and impaired delivery of oxygen to the tissues, with consequent hypoxia. It must be remembered however that hypophosphataemia is almost routine postoperatively but at a level which causes little reduction in 2,3 DPG. Hyperphosphataemia on the other hand increases red blood cell 2,3 DPG.

Regulation of phosphate turnover

This has largely been covered under the section on Ca. Essential hormones for control of PO_4 metabolism are:

1 PTH.
2 $1,25(OH)_2D_3$.
3 Calcitonin.

Less important hormones concerned with PO_4 metabolism are growth hormone, prolactin, corticosteroids and thyroxin. PTH acts on specific cell membrane receptors linked to adenyl cyclase in kidney and bone. It releases cyclic adenosine monophosphate (cAMP) which transmits the stimulus within the cell. In the absence of PTH 90% of PO_4 is reabsorbed in the renal tubule. PTH reduces tubular reabsorption of PO_4, lowers the renal threshold and allows some excretion of PO_4 at lower plasma concentrations. However PTH also stimulates the formation of $1,25(OH)_2D_3$ from $25(OH)D_3$. $1,25(OH)_2D_3$ is responsible for increasing the plasma PO_4 concentration mainly by increasing intestinal absorption. An increase in plasma PO_4 inhibits synthesis of this hormone by negative feedback.

Calcitonin

The same comments apply as for the section on Ca. Calcitonin also acts via adenyl cyclase on the kidney and has a generalised effect reducing tubular absorption of Ca, PO_4, Na, Mg, K and HCO_3.

There is little evidence to show that plasma PO_4 requires such stringent regulation within limits as does Ca and in fact considerable fluctuations occur in plasma PO_4 throughout the day. There are no specific direct mechanisms to control plasma PO_4. It is postulated however that low concentrations of intracellular inorganic phosphorus stimulate the formation of $1,25(OH)_2D_3$ with subsequent increase in Ca and PO_4 absorption from the gut. If ECF Ca is normal this will have the effect of suppressing PTH so the kidney will excrete Ca but PO_4 reabsorption occurs. Impaired renal function has a marked effect on plasma PO_4. A reduction in glomerular filtration rate (GFR) reduces the excretion of PO_4 with hyperphosphataemia.

If tubular function is impaired PO_4 reabsorption is impaired producing hypophosphataemia and PO_4 depletion.

Thyroxine increases bone Ca and PO_4 turnover. Growth hormone increases intestinal absorption of PO_4 and reduces renal tubular reabsorption of PO_4. This is reflected in a small positive PO_4 balance during growth. Active acromegaly may be accompanied by hyperphosphataemia. Glucocorticoids increase PO_4 excretion in the urine.

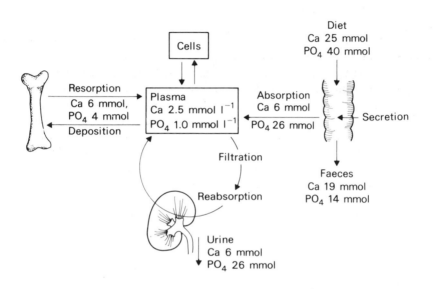

Fig. 4.5 Summary of daily calcium and phosphate turnover showing approximate net values.

MAGNESIUM

Magnesium (Mg) is the eleventh most abundant element in the body, the fourth most abundant cation and the second most abundant intracellular cation after K. 54% of the total Mg is found in bone. Soft tissue Mg is largely intracellular and mainly in the bound form. Normal plasma Mg is $0.7–1.0 \text{ mmol l}^{-1}$; about one third being in the protein bound form.

Table 4.4 Distribution of magnesium in a 70 kg man (mmol).

Bone	610
Soft tissue	500
Extravascular fluid	7
Blood	
plasma	2.5
erythrocytes	5.5
	1125

Plasma Mg within the normal range is not uncommon with a total body Mg depletion which is similar to the situation with K. Normal urine Mg is 2.5–5.0 mmol l^{-1}.

Table 4.5 Constitution of plasma magnesium (mmol l^{-1}).

Free Mg	0.53
Protein bound	0.30
$MgHPO_4$	0.03
Mg citrate	0.04
Other complexes	0.06

Measurement of plasma magnesium

Two methods are available which have been discussed elsewhere:
1   Atomic absorption.
2   Flame spectroscopy. This was the method used prior to the development of atomic absorption spectroscopy.

Daily magnesium turnover

The average daily Mg intake is about 12 mmol largely from green vegetables. Minimum requirement have been put at 3 mmol daily. Such a value is a result of studies of the minimum intake required to prevent negative Mg balance.

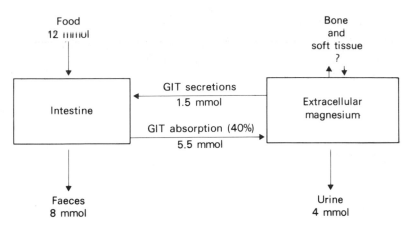

Fig. 4.6   Daily magnesium turnover. Mg MW = 24.32.

Less than half the ingested Mg is absorbed. Faecal losses amount to 8 mmol daily and urine losses to 4 mmol daily although this can be reduced during deprivation to less than 0.5 mmol daily.

About 40–50% of Mg is absorbed from the gut into ECF from which some is excreted in the urine, some is deposited in bone and about 1.5 mmol daily enters gastrointestinal tract secretions. Dietary intake and absorption do influence plasma concentrations of Mg but have little effect on renal excretion. Little is known about the intestinal absorption of Mg. There may be a common mechanism for Mg and Ca absorption since in animal nutrition studies there is competition between Mg and Ca for absorption.

As glucose enters cells stimulated by insulin K, PO_4 and Mg enter as well. It is well known that intravenous infusions of glucose, sorbitol and other carbohydrates may be associated with hypomagnesaemia as well as hypophosphataemia.

Physiological importance of magnesium

Within cells Mg is specifically associated with the function of a number of intracellular structures and organelles.

Enzyme systems

The most clearly defined action of Mg is to activate intracellular enzyme systems. That Mg is found abundantly in pre-Cambrian seas points to the evolutionary importance of this.

ENZYME SYSTEMS ACTIVATED BY Mg

1 All ATPases, alkaline phosphatases and pyrophosphatases. Since ATP is required for all anabolic processes including fat, protein and nucleic acid synthesis and glucose utilisation, Mg is essential for all these functions. There is a good correlation between high metabolic activity within cells and their Mg, K and high energy phosphate content.
2 Thiamine pyrophosphate as cofactor.
3 Enolase.
4 Some peptidases.

Neuromuscular activity

Mg has properties similar to those of Ca. A fall in ECF Mg results in paraesthesia, increased neuromuscular excitability, tetany and cramps. A rise in ECF Mg is associated with muscle weakness, paralysis and cardiorespiratory collapse. Plasma Mg of more than 2.5 mmol l^{-1} inhibits atrioventricular and intraventricular conduction and $8-10$ mmol l^{-1} produces cardiac arrest. Direct application of Mg to central nervous tissue blocks synaptic transmission and at high doses Mg salts produce loss of consciousness. The neuromuscular transmission block is associated with a reduction in amplitude of the end plate potential. Both central and peripheral depression of transmission can be antagonised by Ca.

Fish and invertebrates can be anaesthetised with Mg and returned to consciousness after intravenous Ca. These opposing effects are interesting in view of the similar effect of the two ions on normal excitability; low levels of either producing tetany.

Vascular system

Mg is a peripheral vasodilator which in large doses lowers the blood pressure.

Normal regulation of magnesium

The plasma concentration of Mg is by no means as well controlled as that of Ca and the mechanisms are less well clarified. During Mg depletion plasma concentration can fall by 50% with every few symptoms and a relatively small loss of total Mg.

Factors concerned with normal regulation of magnesium

1 Hormones.
2 Ion balance across cell membranes.
3 The kidney.

HORMONES

Thyroid hormone. Excess thyroid hormone can decrease plasma Mg concentration and is associated with negative Mg balance.

Growth hormone. This causes retention of Mg in bone and soft tissues.

Parathormone. Only PTH seems to be normally concerned with homeostasis.

Aldosterone and vasopressin can influence Mg handling.

As plasma concentration of Mg falls the release of PTH is increased resulting in:
1 Diminished urinary Mg excretion.
2 Increased gastrointestinal absorption of Mg.
However PTH is relatively inefficient at restoring plasma Mg to normal levels probably due to the absence of an efficient feedback mechanism.

ION BALANCE ACROSS CELL MEMBRANES

As Mg is actively taken up into cells the intracellular concentration is maintained at the expense of the ECF concentration. In addition to the well known Na pump there may be a pump to regulate intracellular Mg, Ca ratios. Either Ca is pumped out of the cell or Mg is pumped in or both. Ca often functions as an extracellular activator whereas K and Mg activate intracellular phosphate metabolism.

RENAL EXCRETION

Free Mg is filtered at the glomerulus in an amount which varies with the glomerular filtration rate and the amount bound to plasma protein. Then most of this is reabsorbed in the proximal tubule where PTH stimulates the process. Proximal tubular reabsorption of filtered Ca and Mg is closely related to reabsorption of Na although in conditions of Mg deficiency the excretion of Mg is markedly reduced whilst that of Na remains the same. Active reabsorption of Mg also occurs in the distal tubule and collecting duct against an electrochemical gradient. There may be additional transport mechanisms shared with Ca since increasing the plasma concentration of one ion decreases reabsorption and increases excretion of the other ion.

Appendix to Part I

It is a capital mistake to theorize
before one has data

Memoirs of Sherlock Holmes
SIR ARTHUR CONAN DOYLE

It is now extremely easy to ask for a routine urea and electrolyte (U and E) measurement. Laboratories can process large numbers of blood samples in an autoanalyser, such as SMAC. Unfortunately, vast numbers of normal blood samples are processed for each abnormal one and there is little justification for requesting such an investigation (U and E) unless an abnormality is suspected or extremely likely. In any event, it is essential to know when an abnormality occurs in a routine U and E measurement, what is the total clinical picture affecting the patient at that time, and events interpreted in the light of knowledge of normal control and physiology of blood fluids. This is particularly true when a measurement of urine U and E is requested. The limitations of a random concentration of electrolytes in urine have already been pointed out. It is important in looking at the urinary excretion of electrolytes to collect the total excretion over 24 hours. In certain circumstances these can be extremely helpful in patient management. This will be further discussed in the chapters in Part II.

Although disturbance of ions are considered separately it is very common for a mixed electrolyte abnormality to occur. It is rare to request a plasma level of one particular electrolyte and more often interpretation of the plasma electrolyte profile is required. Instruments for measurement of electrolytes are now extremely sophisticated. Ion selective electrodes are capable of measuring sodium and potassium on as little as 20 microlitres of whole blood. Despite this sophistication a result is only of value, as has already been pointed out, if the sample has been taken meticulously to avoid spurious abnormalities in results. Ion selective electrodes can also be incorporated into catheters for continuous monitoring of electrolytes such as K and Ca in blood or ISF.

In addition advances in measurement have led to estimation of the quantities of loss in the various compartments. Excluding acute blood loss, it is now possible to estimate the category and volume of fluid loss in acutely depleted patients by measurement of the haematocrit and plasma protein concentrations in venous plasma samples. In surgical patients acute depletion of body fluids occurs because plasma or extracellular fluid or a mixture of these fluids is lost. An acute loss of plasma will cause an increase in the concentration of red cells in the vascular compartment, that is to say an increase in haematocrit. In extracellular fluid loss there is no loss of plasma protein from the plasma compartment but only water and electrolyte, therefore the plasma protein concentration will rise. The amount of ECF loss can be calculated from this increase in plasma protein concentration. Therefore measurement of both haematocrit and plasma protein concentration in a situation of acute depletion can enable a distinction to be made between a shrinkage in the plasma compartment alone and a shrinkage in the extracellular space so that logical fluid repletion can take place. These problems will be discussed more fully in Part II.

Such is the sophistication of modern methods that serial total body estimates of the absolute amounts of fat, protein, minerals and water within the body, have been developed for research purposes. After the patient has been weighed and skin fold thickness measured, total body contents of potassium, nitrogen, sodium, chloride, calcium and phosphorus can be measured with a whole body radiation counter after irradiation with fast neutrons. Calculations permit absolute values for the amounts of body fat, proteins, minerals and water. Serial measurements permit determination of the tissue composition of weight loss, establishment of the nature of weight loss, or gain, for example whether this is fat, muscle or water, and permit an evaluation of the effects of parenteral nutrition. This, understandably, is a method totally unsuited to routine monitoring, but it does much to advance our understanding of acute changes in critically ill patients. Before abnormalities of body water and electrolytes are discussed, there follows a number of tables indicating normal values within the human body.

TABLES

A.1 Composition of whole adult body.

A.2 Normal values.

A.3 Intracellular concentrations.

A.4 Composition of secretions.

A.5 Normal urine values.

A.6 Principal urine constituents.

A.7 Typical nitrogen composition of normal urine on 90 g protein diet.

A.8 Sodium, potassium, N_2 and energy content of intravenous fluids.

Table A.1 Composition of whole adult body.

Body weight	70	kg
Water	42	l
Total N_2	2	kg
Protein	12	kg
Sodium	5150	mmol
Potassium	4050	mmol
Chloride	2940	mmol
Calcium	32 500	mmol
Phosphate	22 600	mmol
Magnesium	1125	mmol
Fat	10.5	kg
Carbohydrate	0.5	kg

Table A.2 Normal values. There is some variation between laboratories.

Sodium	133–145 mmol l^{-1}
Potassium	3.5–4.8 mmol l^{-1}
Chloride	95–105 mmol l^{-1}
Bicarbonate	24–32 mmol l^{-1}
Urea	2.5–6.6 mmol l^{-1}
Glucose (random)	2.9–9.4 mmol l^{-1}
Creatinine	44–124 μmol l^{-1}
Uric acid	0.1–0.4 mmol l^{-1}
Albumin	35–50 g l^{-1}
Protein	60–80 g l^{-1}
Calcium	2.2–2.6 mmol l^{-1}
Magnesium	0.7–0.9 mmol l^{-1}
Phosphate	0.8–1.35 mmol l^{-1}
Creatinine clearance	40–75 ml min^{-1} m^{-2}
Arterial blood gases	
pH	7.36–7.42
P_{CO_2}	4.4–6.2 kPa
Base excess mmol l^{-1} ± 2.3	
Standard bicarbonate	23–28 mmol l^{-1}
P_{O_2}	12–15 kPa
Hydrogen ion	36–44 ng l^-
Anions	12±4 mEq l^{-1}
Osmolality	280–295 mosmol kg^{-1}
Colloid osmotic pressure	20–25 mmHg

Table A.3 Intracellular concentrations.

Sodium	10–35 mmol l^{-1}
Potassium	150 mmol l^{-1}
Magnesium	12–18 mmol l^{-1}
Bicarbonate	10–20 mmol l^{-1}
Chloride	5 mmol l^{-1}
Phosphate	31 mmol l^{-1}

Table A.4 Composition of secretions. If visible sweating occurs there is a marked increase in its sodium and chloride concentration.

Secretion	Na	K mmol l^{-1}	Cl	HCO₃	Volume (litres daily)
Parotid saliva	112	19	40	–	1.5
Gastric juice	50	15	140	0–15	2–3
Pancreatic juice	130	5	55	110	0.5–1
Bile	145	5	100	38	0.5–1
Ileal juice	140	11	70	Variable	–
Normal stool	20– 40	30–60	20	–	0.1
Diarrhoea	30–140	30–70	–	20–80	Variable
Insensible sweat	12	10	12	–	0.5

Table A.5 Normal urine values.

Specific gravity	1003–1030
Creatinine/24 hours	8.8–17.7 mmol
Urea clearance	60–95 ml min^{-1}
Glomerular filtration rate (GFR)	105–140 ml min^{-1}
Osmolality	30–1400 mosmol kg^{-1}

Table A.6   Principal urine constituents. In normals these are greatly influenced by dietary intake. All these values will be modified depending upon renal function, the degree of catabolism and the presence of infection.

	Normal	Effect of operation
Water ml	1500	500
	(1000–2500)	
Sodium mmol	70–160	5–20
Potassium mmol	40–120	90–180
Urea g	16–350	20–60

Table A.7   Typical nitrogen composition of normal urine on 90g protein diet.

	g 24 hour^{-1}
Total	14.40
Urea	12.50
Creatinine	0.67
Ammonia	0.44
Uric acid	0.23
Other	0.56

Table A.8 Sodium, potassium, N_2 and energy content of intravenous fluids.

Solution	Na mmol l^{-1}	K mmol l^{-1}	N_2 g l^{-1}	Energy kcal l^{-1}	MJ l^{-1}
Whole blood	77	3	6	–	–
Packed cells (PCV 60%)	55	2	4	–	–
Human Albumin Fraction 5%	145	2	8	–	–
Human Albumin Salt poor 20%	130	10	32	–	–
Haemaccel 3.5%	145	5.1	6.3	–	–
Gelofusine 4% gelatin	146	–	–	–	–
HPPF	150	2	6	–	–
Dextran 70 in 0.9%NaCl	150	–	–	–	–
Dextran 70 in 5% Dext.	–	–	–	190	0.79
Polyfusor phosphates	162	19	–	–	–
Dextrose 10%	–	–	–	380	1.59
Sodium chloride 1.8%	308	–	–	–	–
Viaflex NaCl 0.45%	75	–	–	–	–
Baxter Travenol NaCl 0.225%	37.5	–	–	–	–
$NaHCO_3$ 1.4%	167	–	–	–	–
Polyfusor $NaHCO_3$ 4.2%	500	–	–	–	–
Polyfusor $NaHCO_3$ 8.4%	1000	–	–	–	–
Viaflex Hartmanns	131	5	–	–	–
Viaflex 0.18% NaCl, 4% dextrose, 0.2% KCl	30	27	–	150	0.63
Viaflex 0.18% NaCl, 4% dextrose	30		–	150	0.63
Viaflex 0.9% NaCl + 0.2% KCl	150	27	–	–	–
Viaflex 0.9% NaCl	150	–	–	–	–
Viaflex 5% dextrose + KCl 0.2%	–	27	–	190	0.79
Viaflex 5% dextrose	–	–	–	190	0.79
Aminoplex 12	35	30	12	–	–
Aminoplex 14	35	30	14	–	–
Intralipid 10%	–	–	–	1000	4.62
Intralipid 20%	–	–	–	2000	8.4
Dextrose 20%	–	–	–	750	3.14
Dextrose 40%	–	–	–	1500	6.28
Glucoplex 1600	50	30	–	1600	6.72
Glucoplex 1000	50	30	–	1000	4.2
Vamin glucose	50	20	9.4	650	2.75
Vamin N	50	20	9.4	236	1.0
Potassium phosphate 1 mmol HPO_4, 2 mmol K ml^{-1}	–	2000	–	–	–
Dopram solution 2 mg ml^{-1} in 5% dextrose	–	–	–	190	0.79
Metronidazole	130	–	–	–	–

PART II

Chapter 5
Abnormal Water Balance, and Disturbances of Osmolality

Water balance is closely related to Na balance and to separate the two is to some extent a false distinction. Water balance is largely controlled by Na balance. Water deprivation produces a hypertonic state and water intoxication a hypotonic state. Usually these are synonymous with hyper and hypotonic syndromes.

WATER DEPLETION

This gives rise to thirst so that pure water depletion is often associated with impaired consciousness or occurs in those who cannot voluntarily increase their water intake such as the very young and the very old. A patient willing and able to increase water intake can avoid hypertonicity in the complete absence of antidiuretic hormone (ADH) or the ability to concentrate his urine.

Thirst

Thirst is basic to our existence. It acts as an emergency mechanism to repair acute fluid deficits. Normally drinking is anticipatory of future needs and depends on diet, habit and innate circadian rhythms. It is usually dependent on the current need for water. Symptomatic thirst occurs in response to fluid loss from ECF or ICF. These two fluid compartments have their own controlling mechanisms which act independently of each other but have an additive effect on thirst if activated together.

The immediate stimulus for cellular control is a reduction in the volume of the cells in particular those in the hypothalamus. Cellular volume probably fluctuates between an upper satiety volume and a lower threshold level at which thirst occurs. Normally there is a reserve of body fluid so that the level of hydration is above that at which thirst is stimulated.

91

Hypovolaemia is the second major stimulus to thirst production and aids in maintenance of plasma volume. It is in ECF or hypo-volaemic thirst that the renin-angiotensin system participates to a variable extent. A nephrectomised animal can still respond to some ECF stimuli. Involvement of the renin-angiotensin system in hypovolaemic thirst enables the subject to respond to ECF dehydration in two ways:

1   It promotes drinking.

2   It produces Na and water retention by an angiotensin stimulated increase in aldosterone production. This will also increase Na appetite.

Symptomatic thirst therefore occurs in response to fluid loss. However, thirst may also be pathological in which case it persists although the body is normally or over-hydrated. For confirmation of this diagnosis not only must the fluid intake be shown to be disproportionately high but the trend in fluid balance should be measured. Repeated measurement of weight and urine volume should be made and the presence of oedema sought. Pathological thirst occurs in some cases of diabetes insipidus, in compulsive water drinking, stimulation of the neural thirst mechanism by a high plasma renin, in hypercalcaemia and hypokalaemia, in congestive cardiac failure and in manic depressives treated with lithium. In some cases of chronic renal failure with high plasma renin, angiotensin II and aldosterone there may be marked thirst which may be due either to a direct action of renin on the thirst centre or due to reduction in blood volume. Thirst is then often abolished by bilateral nephrectomy.

Thirst occurs when 2% of the body weight has been lost as water (1.5 l in a 70 kg man).

When water is depleted relative to electrolytes the tonicity of body fluids is increased resulting in stimulation of ADH from the posterior pituitary in addition to thirst. Increased ADH increases reabsorption of free water in the distal renal tubule. A rise of 1 mosmol kg^{-1} in plasma osmolality increases urine osmolality by nearly 100 mosmol. This has been discussed more fully in Chapter 1. Synapses involved in ADH release are cholinergic and thus stimulated by nicotine and acetylcholine. Water depletion will only occur when the thirst mechanism fails.

As water is freely permeable across cell membranes it is lost from all compartments and plasma volume is initally maintained (Fig.

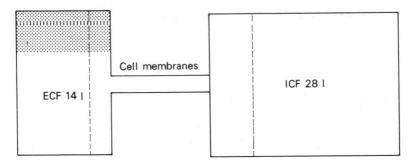

Fig. 5.1 Water deficiency. The effect of 10 litres water loss on body fluid compartments. The dotted lines show the effect of the water loss equally spread between the compartments resulting in an equal increase in osmolality in ECF and ICF. The shaded area donates the intravascular compartment.

5.1). This contrasts sharply with the situation in which a combined loss of salt and water occurs. Peripheral circulatory failure in pure water depletion is a very late manifestation. In fact the plasma compartment may not share to the same extent in the fluid loss because of the increase in colloid osmotic pressure which occurs as water depletion continues. This holds water within the intravascular compartment so that only about 12% of the total water loss is incurred by this compartment.

Biochemical abnormalities

1   Raised Na concentration. The commonest cause of a raised plasma Na concentration is severe water depletion with ECF shrinkage. Values greater than 150 mmol l^{-1} are virtually diagnostic of water loss provided that:
(a) The patient is not receiving an infusion of hypertonic saline.
(b) The patient is not undergoing dialysis against a fluid of abnormally high Na concentration.
    Plasma Na begins to rise in an adult when 3 or more litres of water have been lost.
2   Plasma chloride and urea concentrations increase.
3   Plasma protein levels and haematocrit rise.
4   Urine output falls (less than 500 ml daily) and this urine will have a high specific gravity, osmolality and high urea concentration.

Clinical signs and symptoms of water depletion

    Thirst.
    Sunken cheeks and eyes.
    Weakness.
    Dryness of mucous membranes.
    Reduction of salivary and bronchial secretions.
    Loss of skin turgor.
    Weight loss.

Mental disturbances occur as total body water (TBW) deficit approaches 10%. Many of the effects of hyperosmolality in water deficiency are due to cerebral dehydration when acute osmolar changes are more important than chronic changes since in the later situation the brain is able to generate osmotically active substances (idiogenic osmoles) and hence reduce cellular dehydration. Cerebral dehydration may tear vessels especially in small infants given mannitol and hence may produce subdural or intracerebral haemorrhage. Abnormal neurotransmittor release, reduced energy production or brain cell volume changes depress conscious level and increasing hypertonicity leads to irritability, twitching and convulsions.

Causes of pure water loss

Decreased intake

    Infancy.
    Old age.
    Unconsciousness.
    Dysphagia — carcinoma of the oesophagus.
    Severe nausea and vomiting.
    'Nil by mouth' regime of perioperative surgical patients with inadequate parenteral fluids. Postoperatively if intravenous fluid is withheld a patient will drink about 25 ml kg^{-1} water daily. This amount should therefore be supplied.
    Hyperosmotic diets — these result in a relative water deficit.
    Pathological hypodipsia due to lesions in the supra-opticohypophyseal system are extremely rare but may be associated with disturbance of temperature, appetite and sleep. Insensitvity to pain may accompany this with a possibility of a

good response to naloxone. When ADH secretion is also affected hyperosmolality may be extreme.

Opiates appear to be concerned with ADH secretion. If volunteers are deprived of water, infusion of an analogue of metenkephalin (an endogenous opiate peptide) produces a diuresis attenuated by naloxone. In hydrated subjects this does not occur. Following administration of synthetic metenkephalin plasma immunoreactive ADH levels fail to increase despite hypertonic saline infusion. Therefore opiates appear to suppress osmotically mediated release of ADH. However beta-endorphin can cause secretion of ADH in man: an effect which can be reversed by naloxone. The overall effect of opiate peptides therefore requires further elucidation.

Increased water loss

LUNGS

Marked hyperventilation may accompany fever and cerebral damage after head injury increasing water loss from the lung. In addition extreme breathlessness may limit intake. Patients receiving intermittent positive pressure ventilation must be adequately humidified otherwise considerable water loss will occur.

SKIN

Evaporation of water from the skin surface is a normal temperature regulating mechanism. However, in high environmental temperatures or thyrotoxicosis several litres of hypotonic fluid may be lost daily through the skin.

RENAL LOSSES

Increased urine flow

1   Osmotic diuresis due to mannitol, hyperglycaemia or urea. This has been discussed in Chapter 1. The presence of a non reabsorbable solute in the glomerular filtrate results in passage of a large volume of hypotonic urine with subsequent net water loss.

2   Diuretics. These are discussed in Chapter 14.

Renal tubular defects. These are discussed in Chapter 11.

Diabetes insipidus (DI). This disorder is due either to a defect in ADH production or a defect in the renal response to ADH (nephrogenic DI).

Central diabetes insipidus

This is due to damage in the region of the hypothalamic pituitary system.

CAUSES OF CENTRAL DIABETES INSIPIDUS

Tumour:
  primary — usually a craniopharyngioma
  secondary.
Trauma:
  head injury
  post hypophysectomy.
Infection:
  meningitis
  encephalitis.
Others:
  cerebral sarcoidosis
  Hand-Schüller-Christian disease.
Some of these are accompanied by a disturbance of thirst. Thirst is pathological and produces marked polydipsia and this may be accompanied by malaise and nausea.

Traumatic DI accounts for about 40% of all cases of DI and has a triphasic onset.

1 Polyuria occurs due to insufficient ADH.

2 Uncontrolled release of ADH may occur when the high fluid intake prescribed for the polyuric phase could result in hyponatraemia and water intoxication.

3 1–7 days later DI reappears. This may be permanent or transient since regeneration of ADH production can occur months after the initial injury.

DRUGS

Certain drugs such as alcohol, lithium and narcotic analgesics inhibit ADH release.

In central diabetes insipidus the pathology may also produce a disorder of thirst and this will determine the clinical picture. Patients with reduced or absent ADH secretion and normal thirst mechanisms present with polyuria, polydipsia and *normal* plasma osmolality. Patients with reduced or absent ADH and impaired thirst mechanisms do not have polydipsia but develop plasma *hyperosmolality*.

Usually a patient with DI can concentrate his urine to a maximum of 300 mosmol kg^{-1} but will have some polyuria and excess water loss. Most patients excrete a dilute urine despite dehydration but can concentrate their urine in response to exogenous ADH. Nocturia usually occurs and helps to distinguish DI from psychogenic polydipsia.

DIAGNOSIS OF CENTRAL DIABETES INSIPIDUS

1   The time-hallowed water deprivation test may reveal the diagnosis. Fluid restriction is continued until the patient has lost 3–5% of his body weight or urine osmolality is constant in 3 hourly urine specimens. Five units of subcutaneous ADH are then given and urine is collected for 2 hours. In DI this manoeuvre will produce an increase in urine osmolality. In nephrogenic DI or psychogenic polydipsia there is no change in urine osmolality.

2   Water deprivation is not acceptable to many clinicians who use the response to intramuscular vasopressin tannate in oil.

3   This has now to a large extent been replaced by intranasal synthetic deamino-D-arginine-vasopressin (desmopressin, DDAVP). This form of ADH is also a valuable agent for therapy.

4   Infusion of hypertonic saline can be used to osmotically stimulate ADH release and separate those patients with normal osmoregulation of ADH secretion from those with central DI. If causes of polyuria cannot be established by simple dehydration then measurement of ADH during infusion of hypertonic saline will distinguish between those with normal osmotically stimulated ADH release and those without. In normal individuals a strong positive correlation exists between plasma osmolality and plasma

ADH levels whereas a subnormal ADH response occurs in central DI.

Nephrogenic diabetes insipidus

Two mechanisms may be involved:
1 The distal tubule and collecting duct lose the capacity to respond to ADH although the generation of the medullary osmotic gradient is normal.
2 Generation of the osmotic gradient itself may be impaired. Some drugs may reduce renal concentrating ability (Table 5.1).

Table 5.1 Drugs which reduce renal concentrating ability.

Lithium
Tetracyclines
Methoxyflurane (fluoride ions)
Sulphonylureas
Amphotericin B
Colchicine

In addition hypercalcaemia and hypokalaemia reduce concentrating ability. Management of DI is considered after general treatment of water deficiency.

CALCULATION OF WATER DEFICIT

Body water deficit = normal body water − current body water

Normal body water can be calculated from a knowledge of approximate normal body weight:

Normal body water = 0.6 × normal body weight (kg)

Current body water may be calculated thus:

$$\frac{\text{Normal plasma Na} \times \text{normal body water}}{\text{measured plasma Na}}$$

For example in a 70 kg man with a normal plasma Na ($140 \text{ mmol } l^{-1}$) and a measured Na of 150 mmol l^{-1}

$$\text{Body water deficit} = (0.6 \times 70) - \frac{(140 \times 0.6 \times 70)}{150}$$

$$= 42 - \frac{(140 \times 42)}{150}$$

$$= 42 - 39.2 = 2.8 \text{ litres}$$

Since the deficit is one of pure water total body solute remains the same. Hence:

Normal body water $\times$ normal osmolality
= present body water $\times$ present osmolality.

Normal body water can be calculated as discussed and normal osmolality is 285 mosmol kg^{-1}.

If for example a 70 kg man has a measured osmolality of 310 mosmol kg^{-1} this gives the following:

$$0.6 \times 70 \times 285 = \text{present body water} \times 310$$

$$\text{Present body water} = \frac{0.6 \times 70 \times 285}{310}$$

$$= \frac{1197}{31} = 38.6 \text{ litres}$$

Therefore:

$$\text{Body water deficit} = (0.6 \times 70) - 38.6$$
$$= 42 - 38.6 = 3.4 \text{ litres}$$

A simplified version of this depends on the principle that the % reduction in body water will be proportional to the % increase in plasma Na. However in some cases of dehydration plasma Na is normal and this is unhelpful.

Treatment

It is essential to distinguish clinically between water deficit and Na excess (see also Chapter 6). Clearly treatment must be that of the underlying condition in addition to replacing deficits and continuing losses.

Water replacement

Water may be given orally if the patient can drink or via a nasogastric tube if it can be absorbed and there is no risk to the airway. 48 hours should be allowed for correcting a water deficit. It is very important to avoid overhydration since the cerebral idiogenic osmoles which were produced during dehydration will now act to draw water into cells and produce cerebral oedema with convulsions and a deteriorating conscious level. More often this occurs with overenthusiastic intravenous therapy since this route of repletion is almost always needed in more severe cases.

Solutions available include hpotonic saline such as 0.45% NaCl and 5% dextrose. Prior to infusion 5% dextrose is isotonic: following intravenous infusion the dextrose is metabolised to carbon dioxide (CO_2) and water so that water is effectively supplied without electrolytes.

MONITORING

The patient should be weighed daily and fluid balance accurately measured. In an adult the aim is a urine volume of at least 1000 ml. Unfortunately in the absence of catheterisation accurate urine measurement may be surprisingly difficult.

The conscious level is a valuable guide to the rate and adequacy of replacement.

Laboratory tests. Repeated measurements should be made of haematocrit urea and electrolyte levels to ensure gradual controlled correction.

Following calculation of the fluid deficit replacement should be as follows:

$\frac{1}{3}$ in the first 6 hours.

$\frac{1}{3}$ in the subsequent 18 hours.

$\frac{1}{3}$ in the next 24 hours.

In addition to the deficit, allowance must also be made for continuing losses and basal requirements. However, if the patient is elderly an additional 24–48 hours may be required to safely correct the deficit. If the conscious level first improves and then worsens again cerebral oedema shuld be suspected which if severe may require therapy with intravenous mannitol to reduce intracranial pressure.

Specific treatment: central diabetes insipidus

1 Antidiuretic hormone.
2 ADH analogues.
3 Other drugs.

In the acute situation aqueous vasopressin (ADH) 5–20 units intramuscularly should be given at least twice daily. This may be dangerous in patients with heart disease because it produces arteriolar constriction with hypertension and acute venous (splanchnic) constriction which increases circulating blood volume. Urine output and thirst are helpful in timing of dosage.

ADH ANALOGUES

l-deamino 8-D-arginine vasopressin (DDAVP) is available as a nasal solution. It has twice the duration of action of lysine vasopressin and may be given in a dose of 10–20 μg once or twice daily. DDAVP is supplied in a dropper bottle with a calibrated catheter for intranasal instillation. Each 0.1 ml contains 10 μg and detailed instructions are supplied for the method of administration. Although the oxytoxic effect of this solution is very low it should be used with great caution in pregnant patients. DDAVP injection is also available, and may be given intramuscularly or intravenously in a dose of 1–4 μg daily.

Lysine vasopressin is shorter acting than DDAVP and is given intranasally 5–20 units, 3–7 times daily. It is available in a meter dose spray (2.5 units per squeeze).

Some drugs can decrease renal diluting capacity and may be useful in mild cases of central DI.

1 Thiazide diuretics (useful for nephrogenic DI also).
2 Chlorpropamide.
3 Carbamazepine.
4 Clofibrate.

Chronic administration of thiazide diuretics can reduce urine volume by 50%. Other diuretics or salt restriction produce a similar result. However if salt is added to therapy this antidiuresis does not occur. In fact a negative salt balance (Na depletion) is essential for this effect. A reduction in GFR occurs with enhanced Na reabsorption in the proximal tubule so that a reduced amount of filtrate reaches the distal tubule and urine volume is reduced. There is no effect on plasma ADH level. Chlorpropamide has no effect on ADH levels either and is ineffective in nephrogenic DI. The effect of chlorpropamide is to enhance the peripheral action of ADH by sensitising the renal tubules to the action of endogenous ADH. Chlorpropamide is given in a dose of 250 mg once to twice daily, initially increase to a maximun of 1000 mg daily. This dose also increases thirst. Chlorpropamide may be used in conjunction with a thiazide diuretic. Carbamazepine probably acts in the same way as chlorpropamide and is used in a dose of 200 mg once or twice daily.

It must be stressed that pure water depletion is *rare* and much more commonly mixed salt and water depletion occur.

WATER EXCESS; WATER INTOXICATION

When the body accumulates excess water compared to electrolyte, hypoosmolality occurs. Initially this excess water is distributed throughout the body and little change in plasma electrolyte levels occurs. Progressive water accumulation leads to a small increase in ECF volume without oedema and a progressive fall in plasma Na. Very low levels of plasma Na (less than 120 mmol l^{-1}) usually imply some ECF salt loss as well as water excess.

Clinical features

Symptoms depend on the severity and speed of development of the hypoosmolality. Plasma Na less than 120 mmol l^{-1} is associated with neurological abnormalities only partly related to the development of cerebral oedema. The following clinical features may be present:

　　Confusion, disorientation.
　　Restlessness.
　　Headache, cerebral oedema.
　　Convulsions, nocturnal jerks, muscular cramps.
　　Coma.

Biochemical features

1   Low plasma Na and Cl.
2   Low haematocrit, haemoglobin and plasma proteins.
3   In most instances urine Na is greater than 20 mmol l^{-1}.

Causes of water excess

Increased water intake

1   Pathological hyperdipsia.
2   Ill advised fluid regimes. During the postoperative period when the stress response to trauma occurs the kidney has a reduced ability to excrete free water. Administration of 5% dextrose in this situation will effectively supply more water and worsen the situation. If blood or ECF volume deficits have been inadequately replaced then the production of ADH and aldosterone will be stimulated.
3   Water absorption during bladder irrigation is rare now that 1.5% glycine solutions are used for irrigation. This solution is almost isotonic and reduces the dangers of haemolysis following water absorption. However severe hyponatraemia and ECG changes which include a wide QRS of increased amplitude, T wave inversion and bradycardia are still reported.

Inability to excrete water normally

1   Inappropriate secretion of ADH from the hypothalamus or pituitary region. Plasma osmolality is low.
2   Inappropriate secretion of a similar peptide from a neoplasm for example carcinoma of the bronchus or pancreas.
3   Adrenal insufficiency.
4   Hypothyroidism.
5   Pain and emotion.
6   Drugs.
(a) Those which act centrally to reduce renal diluting capacity:
   Nicotine.
   Narcotics.
   Sulphonylureas.
   Clofibrate.
   Carbamazepine.
   Vincristine.

(b) Those which act on the kidney to reduce renal diluting capacity:
   Diuretics.
   Sulphonylureas.
   Biguanides.
   Antiinflammatory drugs such as aspirin, paracetamol.
   Diazoxide.
Experimentally angiotensin II when injected into specific regions of
the hypothalamus may produce either drinking of water, release of
ADH or rises in blood pressure.

Transfer of water from cells

Strictly this is not a situation of true water excess. It occurs in the
following circumstances:
1   Uncontrolled diabetes mellitus.
2   Administration of mannitol.
   A sudden rise in blood glucose draws intracellular water into ECF
diluting plasma constituents. For every 3 mmol l^{-1} elevation of
plasma glucose these is a decrease of 1 mmol l^{-1} in plasma Na by
osmotic dilution. However, such circumstances lead to an osmotic
diuresis such that dehydration and increased plasma osmolality
result. Transfer of water from cells therefore is a very short lived
phenomenon.

Hyperdipsia

Pathological hyperdipsia may be due to a psychiatric disturbance.
Hypoosmolality can occur if the renal diluting capacity is impaired
by drugs or renal disease. A central nervous system lesion such as
tumour, trauma or inflammation within the hypothalamic thirst
area will produce the same result.
   Hypercalcaemia and hypokalaemia increase thirst but the associated polyuria prevents hypoosmolality. Drugs such as thioridazine
and chlorpropamide increase thirst. Any circumstance in which the
function of the countercurrent mechanism is impaired will reduce
renal diluting capacity.

ADH excess syndromes

ADH secretion may occur in the presence of hypoosmolality when nonosmotic stimuli lower the threshold of secretion. This may occur when the effective ECF volume is reduced in oedematous states for example heart failure, hypoalbuminaemia, venous and lymphatic obstruction. This inappropriate ADH secretion is *uncommon*.

Conditions associated with pathological ADH production

PULMONARY

Carcinoma
Pneumonia
Abscess.
Aspergillosis.
Tuberculosis.
Other intrathoracic conditions may also be associated with this syndrome: these include thymoma, post mitral valvotomy, artificial ventilation and severe prolonged asthma.

CENTRAL NERVOUS SYSTEM DISEASE

Viral and bacterial encephalitis and meningitis.
Cerebrovascular accident.
Cerebral tumour, abscess.
Trauma.
Guillain Barré syndrome.

DRUGS

MISCELLANEOUS

Leukaemia, Hodgkin's disease.
Porphyria.
Stress.
Although many drugs reduce renal ability to produce dilute urine there is little evidence of an abnormal ADH level. Traditionally carcinoma of the bronchus is the commonest cause of this syndrome but in a recent series chest infection was a commoner cause and all patients had a rasied ADH level. There is increasing interest in the role of the renin angiotensin system in regulation of thirst, ADH

release and sodium homeostasis. It appears that a separate intrinsic cerebral renin angiotensin system exists in which angiotensin mediates ADH release.

The increase in ADH results initially in volume expansion which leads to the following:

1   Increased renal perfusion, increased GFR and decreased proximal tubular reabsorption of Na and water.
2   Increased renal medullary blood flow and washout of the hypertonic medulla.
3   Suppression of aldosterone.
4   Hyponatraemia *per se* interferes directly with the action of ADH on collecting ducts, with the result that a Na diuresis occurs and a new steady state is set up. Volume expansion is therefore corrected but hyponatraemia remains. This is asymptomatic hyponatraemia unless water intoxication develops.

There has been some confusion regarding measured levels of ADH in these conditions, but the following are good criteria for diagnosing inappropriate ADH secretion:

1   Hyponatraemia with reduced plasma and ECF osmolality.
2   Continued Na excretion.
3   Normal ECF volume.
4   Urine not maximally dilute.
5   Normal renal and adrenal function.

Variation in assay methods and normal ranges and failure to correlate ADH level to plasma osmolality may account for some reports of the totally erratic ADH production. In this syndrome it does seem that some response to osmotic stimuli remains and there is evidence for the resetting of the osmostat to a new steady state with normal operation of other factors which influence water excretion. It is important to remember that inappropriate ADH secretion is *rare* and much more often hyponatraemia is due to iatrogenic water intoxication when 5% dextrose is infused in excessive amounts.

In adrenal insufficiency and hypothyroidism there is inability to excrete a water load which responds to specific treatment of the underlying condition. Oxytocin infusions like ADH analogues decrease urine diluting ability and can cause hypoosmolality especially if the oxytocin is administered in excessive volumes of 5% dextrose.

Treatment

For all causes of water excess treatment of the underlying cause is most important. Mild cases of water excess may be treated by withholding water and permitting only 600–1000 ml daily to cover insensible losses. Many of the causes of inappropriate ADH secretion are short lived and self limiting. If severe life threatening central nervous system symptoms develop, however, such as convulsions, simple water restriction will be inadequate. In such circumstances one approach is to give a combination of a diuretic such as frusemide with a small volume of hypertonic saline (1.8% NaCl). The hypertonic saline will expand ECF volume hence the importance of the diuretic to induce a negative water balance. In an emergency 8.4% $NaHCO_3$ solution is a more readily available hypertonic solution. This form of treatment is dangerous in the elderly because of the risk of heart failure due to circulatory overload. In addition patients are already volume expanded and in the presence of normal renal function the Na will be excreted so that hyponatraemia and cerebral oedema may recur. Alternative forms of therapy for treatment of chronic or pesistent inappropriate ADH secretion should be reserved for situations in which water restriction fails:

1 Lithium.
2 Demethylchlortetracycline.

These two agents interfere with cellular action of ADH and produce nephrogenic DI in man. They interfere with the normal ADH mediated stimulation of adenyl cyclase to increase cyclic AMP production in the renal tubules. In man demethylchlortetracycline (demeclocyline) 600–1200 mg daily is superior to lithium and may obviate the need for water restriction. This drug has also been used for chronic oedema in cirrhotic patients when it induces a substantial increase in Na and water excretion. The increase in Na excretion is independent of ADH and may be due to interference with the action of aldosterone. The patient should be followed up closely. A rise in blood urea and creatinine due to tetracyclines is not uncommon since they have a catabolic action but the possibility of a nephrotoxic effect should always be kept in mind. Ethanol acts centrally to suppress ADH release when this is due to a neurohypophyseal source of ADH rather than an ectopic source but has obvious limitations for long term treatment. The ideal drug for the treatment of this condition would be a competitive inhibitor of the action of ADH.

In summary, water restriction is the treatment of choice for this syndrome but in the acutely symptomatic or the chronic syndrome one of these alternative therapies should be considered.

As this syndrome includes such a variety of aetiological factors in which the increase in ADH secretion is not always inappropriate (it is a normal finding in stress) and as the pathophysiology is not totally clear some authors suggest abandoning this nomenclature and describing the clinical circumstances for example hyponatraemia associated with carcinoma of the bronchus.

DISORDERS OF OSMOREGULATION

These have been referred to as they occured in this chapter and Chapter 6, but will be considered here for the sake of completeness.

Hypoosmolality

This is due either to:
1   Water overload, or
2   Solute loss.

Symptoms occur with a plasma osmolality less than 250 mosmol kg^{-1} or plasma Na less than 120 mmol l^{-1} and include headache, anorexia, nausea and vomiting, irritability, restlessness and weakness. At a plasma Na less than 110 mmol l^{-1} confusion and convulsions develop. Death occurs when plasma osmolality is less than 210 mosmol kg^{-1}. Cardiovascular function is preserved but if plasma osmolality is very low pulmonary oedema may occur. Management of water excess is discussed above and solute loss in Chapter 6.

Hyperosmolality

This is due to either:
1   Increase in solute, or
2   Water loss.

Total ECF solute in a 70 kg man is less than 4000 mosmol. The solute load from hypertonic solutions may be enormous as in the following examples:

Dextrose 50%   2525 mosmol kg^{-1}
Mannitol 20%   1099 mosmol kg^{-1}.

Impermeant solutes such as mannitol and sorbitol increase plasma osmolar load but, of greater importance, they induce hypotonic fluid losses by producing an osmotic diuresis. Causes of water loss have been discussed above.

Table 5.2 Cause of solute overload

Solute	Cause
Glucose	Hyperosmolar non-ketotic coma
	Intravenous feeding
Urea	Renal failure
Sodium	Intravenous feeding
	Infant feeding
	Saline enema
Mannitol, glycerol	
Sucrose, sorbitol	Overadministration
Fructose	
Alcohol	Rare

Symptoms of hyperosmolality include thirst, tachycardia, hypotension and hyperthermia. Cerebral dehydration causes confusion, hallucinations and coma with convulsions. Symptoms occur at a plasma osmolality greater than 320 mosmol kg^{-1}. Hyperosmolality implies cellular dehydration. In this respect brain cells in the human appear to be unique in that they generate idiogenic osmoles during states of dehydration and hyperosmolality. In experimental hypernatraemia brain volume is substantially reduced after one hour but after 7 days it has returned to its normal size in the presence of continued hypernatraemia. Where therefore does this new intracellular solute to increase brain cell volume come from? Half apparently is ECF Na, K and Cl, which move into the cell. The other half is new solute generated within the cell, at least some of which is amino acid. In experimental hyperglycaemia it takes only 4 hours for the brain volume to return to normal and for idiogenic osmoles to be identified. If dehydration is excessively rapid there is no time for development of these idiogenic osmoles but equally correction of hyperosmolality overrapidly may result in intracellular oedema since these idiogenic osmoles cannot be removed or inactivated fast enough.

Sudden ECF hyperosmolality increases ECF volume and may produce pulmonary oedema. Usually hyperosmolality is due to water and *some* salt loss so that a combination of ECF and some ICF depletion occurs. Pure water loss is relatively rare. If it is profound enough to produce shock it will cause severe hypernatraemia with a Na concentration greater than 170 mmol l^{-1}. If plasma Na is less than this then in the presence of hypotension salt and water has been lost. In other words hypotonic loss has occurred.

The combination of ECF volume depletion and hyperosmolality both stimulate ADH secretion. Water retention occurs to restore osmolality towards normal.

Thirst is also stimulated and increases water intake (without salt) in the presence of the increase in ADH. This may rarely actually produce hypoosmolality.

Table 5.3 Abnormalities of osmolality.

Diagnosis	Test	Measurement	Reading mosmol kg^{-1}
Normal		Plasma osmolality	280–295
	Water deprivation (after 8 hours)	Plasma osmolality	300
		Urine osmolality	600
Diabetes insipidus	Water deprivation (after 8 hours)	Plasma osmolality	300
		Urine osmolality	270
		U:P osmolality ratio	0.9–1.0
Inappropriate ADH secretion		Plasma Na concentration	125 mmol l^{-1}
		Plasma osmolality	270

Treatment

Treatment is to replace any losses with the appropriate fluid over 2–3 days to avoid isotonic water intoxication. These aspects are discussed elsewhere. Hyperglycaemia as a cause of hyperosmolality is discussed under diabetes in Chapter 14.

Chapter 6
Abnormal Sodium
and Chloride Balance

Acute disturbances of electrolyte balance produce nonspecific symptoms and hence are difficult to detect clinically. Their presence is often suspected when a 'routine urea and electrolyte' request returns an abnormal result. In view of this it is essential to fully evaluate a patient clinically when such an abnormal result is found.

Clinical problems of salt balance are exemplified by changes in extracellular fluid (ECF) volume. Plasma Na concentration only reflects the ratio between total ECF Na and total ECF water and abnormalities of plasma Na can be due to changes in either or both these compartments.

Normally plasma Na is maintained within narrow limits ($\pm 2\%$) by varying water intake and renal Na excretion. Following salt loss and reduced plasma Na thirst and ADH secretion are inhibited and initially plasma Na is preserved but at the expense of ECF volume. The kidney can reduce Na excretion to as little as 5 mmol l^{-1} in severe Na retention and following a salt load can excrete as much as 250 mmol l^{-1} Na.

HYPONATRAEMIA

An enormous number of pathological states can produce hyponatraemia. The effects of such a state will vary with the speed of onset of the electrolyte abnormality. Severe hyponatraemia of rapid onset may be fatal, producing cerebral oedema within hours, rapidly followed by coma and convulsions. This is a situation with a 50% mortality. Slowly developing hyponatraemia, however, may produce minimal effects, and a plasma Na as low as 89 mmol l^{-1} in a conscious patient has been recorded.

Definition of hyponatraemia

Plasma Na concentration less than 130 mmol l^{-1}.

It is essential to distinguish between true hyponatraemia and pseudohyponatraemia. A spuriously low Na (pseudohyponatraemia) may occur when a large amount of solid matter is present in the plasma, chiefly as lipids or protein. Electrolytes are present only in the aqueous phase of plasma but their concentration is measured and expressed as mmol per total volume of plasma. The lipid volume of plasma is expanded in conditions of diabetic ketosis, nephrotic syndrome and during lipid infusions. If, for example, 20% of the plasma volume is occupied by lipid and the measured concentration of Na is 120 mmol l^{-1} then the true plasma Na is 150 mmol l^{-1}. All obviously lipaemic plasma should be ultracentrifuged before analysis. Measurement of plasma concentrations of lipids is not routine but there are ways of ensuring that pseudohyponatraemia does not exist.

Methods of assessing hyponatraemia

1 Measurement of plasma osmolality. A calculated plasma osmolality is valueless since it depends on the apparent plasma Na.
2 Plasma levels of other electrolytes such as K, Cl and HCO_3 will also be low in hyperlipidaemia.
3 Urine measurements may be of some value provided there is no renal salt losing syndrome. This is discussed further later in this chapter.
4 The use of an ion selective electrode (ISE) electrolyte analyser which does not dilute plasma prior to measurement, for example the Nova Biomedical 'Nova I'. This machine measures the activity of ions in plasma water and therefore is independent of lipids and proteins which reduce the plasma water space. Unfortunately there are few such machines available at present and they are expensive.

Symptoms of hyponatraemia

Symptoms are rare until plasma Na is less than 120 mmol l^{-1}.

Headache.
Muscle cramps and weakness.
Thirst.
Nausea.
Agitation.

Anorexia.
Disorientation.
Apathy.
Lethargy.

As plasma Na continues to fall to $< 110 \text{ mmol l}^{-1}$ then drowsiness progresses to coma with convulsions. Tendon reflexes may then be diminished and rigidity, extensor plantar responses and pseudobulbar palsy may be found.

Hyponatraemia is a laboratory abnormality. The way in which this is related to the clinical state of the patient and his subsequent management depend on the state of the ECF volume. Hyponatraemia can occur with a diminished, expanded or normal ECF volume.

Hyponatraemia with decreased ECF volume

Causes

EXCESSIVE Na LOSS

From the gastrointestinal tract.
Nausea.
Vomiting.
Diarrhoea.
Fistulae.
Gastric aspiration.
Hidden losses in ileus and intestinal obstruction.

From the kidney.
Salt losing conditions.
Excessive diuretic therapy.
Polycystic renal disease.
Medullary cystic disease.
Nephrocalcinosis.
Analgesic nephropathy.
Interstitial nephritis.
Post-obstructive diuresis as an acute situation.
The diuretic phase of an acute tubular necrosis.
Administration of Mannitol or Dextran.
Hyperglycaemia (osmotic diuretic effect).

Adrenal insufficiency.

Severe alkalosis. In these circumstances increased urinary loss of bicarbonate necessitates an accompanying cation (Na).

Skin.

Severe sweating.

Burns.

Exfoliative dermatitis.

Exudates.

Peritonitis.

Pancreatitis.

Excessive removal of serous effusions, for example ascites.

Trauma.

Sequestration of ECF occurs in severely traumatised limbs. If these fluid 'losses' are replaced with hypotonic fluid, hyponatraemia will occur.

These salt losses are almost always associated with water loss as well and variable potassium loss. The diagnosis of such salt losses is not especially difficult but if another solute such as glucose is present in excess, this will tend to hold water in ECF and the severity of the situation may be underestimated. When hyperglycaemia is treated, the degree of salt deficiency and ECF depletion may be unmasked.

DECREASED INTAKE

This is rare and usually iatrogenic such as occurs when acute losses due to sweating or from the gastrointestinal tract are replaced with 5% dextrose only.

When hyponatraemia occurs with a reduced ECF volume the following clinical signs occur:

Postural hypotension.

Low pulse volume.

Reduced central venous pressure.

Loss of skin turgor.

Reduced eyeball tension.

Dry skin and mucous membranes.

Peripheral vasoconstriction.

Oliguria.

If the losses are not replaced the situation progresses to the shock state and metabolic acidosis will accompany these clinical signs (see Chapters 10 and 13).

The salt loss is initially from the plasma volume and ECF compartment, tending to render it hypoosmolar, so that water passes into cells to maintain osmotic equilibrium. This produces the severe reduction in ECF volume required to produce the clinical signs. In order to maintain the cardiac output the following changes occur:

1 Pulse rate and peripheral resistance rise due to increased sympathetic nervous system activity.

2 The renin angiotensin system is activated by one of the following mechanisms:

(a) Sympathetic nervous system.

(b) Catecholamines.

(c) Decreased Na concentration in the macula densa.

This results in increased angiotensin II production with further vasoconstriction, increased aldosterone production and Na retention.

3 Increased ADH secretion.

Laboratory findings

BLOOD

Haemoglobin, haematocrit, plasma proteins and urea are all raised.

URINE

Osmolality, specific gravity, creatinine and urea are all increased. Urine Na will be decreased to less than 10 mmol l^{-1} unless there is an intrinsic salt losing problem when the Na will be greater than 30 mmol l^{-1}. Even in these circumstances, if the disturbance is severe enough to cause a reduction in renal perfusion then renal Na will again be low.

Estimation of sodium deficit

Most of the total body Na is in the ECF, which is roughly 20% of the body weight. An estimate of the Na deficit may be obtained therefore by the following formula:

$$\text{Na deficit} = (\text{normal plasma Na} - \text{measured plasma Na}) \times 0.2 \times \text{body wt in kg}$$

A 70 kg man, in whom the normal plasma Na should be 140 mmol l^{-1} and measured Na is in fact 120 mmol l^{-1}, has a Na deficit of

$$(140 - 120) \times 0.2 \times 70$$
$$= 20 \times 14 = 280 \text{ mmol}$$

Such an estimation however is not accurate and must serve as a guide only since it takes no account of shifts in water into and out of the ECF by osmosis which occur with changes in ECF Na concentration in order to maintain isotonicity between body fluid compartments. Most patients who are fluid depleted in fact have mixed salt and water losses. The extent of fluid depletion can be correlated with the clinical circumstances.

Table 6.1 Loss of body fluids as percentage of body weight.

	Adults	Children (6 months to 6 years of age)
Mild	4.0	5.0
Moderate	6.0	7.5
Severe	8.0	10.0

Mild salt and water depletion rarely exhibits signs of cardiovascular system dysfunction but these become apparent as depletion becomes moderate and with severe depletion there will be tachycardia and extreme hypotension.

Management of hyponatraemia with ECF depletion

Losses require correction. In acute circumstances of Na loss it is rarely possible to replace adequately by the oral route, therefore intravenous replacement is required. The replacement fluid should correspond as closely as possible to the fluid lost, for example, Hartmann's solution is appropriate for gastrointestinal losses and plasma for burns. Hypertonic saline should be avoided and most commonly 0.9% Na Cl is used. Losses should be replaced slowly since equilibrium across the blood brain barrier (BBB) is slow so that rapid replacement may lead to disequilibration and deterioration in central nervous system signs. Oral supplements may be more valuable in the stable situation of renal salt losing syndromes.

Estimated losses are a guide only and the repletion may have to be modified due to continued losses or for example development of endotoxinaemia. Although this book does not deal with paediatric fluid balance, it is pertinent to mention here that oral therapy can be undertaken in dehydrated infants with the standard WHO (World Health Organisation)/UNICEF glucose electrolyte solution.

Table 6.2   Composition of WHO/UNICEF glucose electrolyte solution.

	mmol l^{-1}
Na	90
K	20
Cl	180
HCO_3	30
Glucose	111

Proper use of this solution will rehydrate severely depleted infants without any risk of electrolyte overload.

Hyponatraemia with clinically normal extracellular fluid volume

This is usually due to water retention (see Chapter 5) and total body Na is normal. There may in fact be a small increase in ECF volume but insufficient to be detected clinically. Na handling by the kidney is usually normal and urine Na is greater than 20 mmol l^{-1}. In other words the urinary Na reflects the dietary intake. If ECF depletion occurs for any other reason, the kidney can retain Na. Sustained release of ADH occurs despite low plasma Na concentration. This whole subject is discussed more fully in Chapter 5.

Causes of hyponatraemia with clinically normal ECF volume

1   Excessive ADH.
2   Glucocorticoid deficiency, Addison's disease.

3 Severe hypothyroidism.
4 Diuretics.
5 Water overload with normal renal function.

Excessive ADH production has been discussed elsewhere. In glucocorticoid deficiency one of the main features is inability to excrete a water load. Replacement of the normal physiological concentrations of steroid restores the kidney's ability to excrete dilute urine. The action of steroid in these circumstances may be a direct effect on the osmoreceptors in the hypothalamus or a permissive action on collecting ducts, making them sensitive to ADH and impermeable to water.

Diuretics usually cause isosmotic Na excretion. Hyponatraemia may occur, however, in the following circumstances:

(a) ECF volume contraction which stimulates ADH secretion.
(b) Impaired urinary dilution when diuretics block Na reabsorption from cortical diluting segments.
(c) Potassium deficiency.
(d) Thirst resulting in increased hypotonic oral fluid intake.
(e) Overdiuresis, resulting in excess salt and water loss and its replacement by hypotonic fluid.
(f) Possible increased tubular sensitivity to ADH.

Infusion of Mg in diuretic induced hyponatraemia in severe congestive cardiac failure results in a rise in plasma Na probably due to the effect of Mg on membrane ATPase.

BEER DRINKERS' HYPONATRAEMIA

Consumption of 5 litres of more of beer daily is being increasingly recognised as a cause of hyponatraemia. Beer has a low Na content (2 mmol l^{-1}) and if the diluting ability of the kidney (30 mosmol kg^{-1}) is exceeded, then effectively water retention occurs.

Management

Management is that of the underlying condition (see Chapter 5). Usually fluid restriction corrects hyponatraemia, but the value of this is an asymptomatic patient with minimal expansion of ECF volume is questionable.

Hyponatraemia with expansion of ECF volume

In this situation total ECF Na may be considerably increased but ECF water increases proportionately more resulting in hyponatraemia. Retention of Na is associated with the inability to excrete water normally. Oedema usually accompanies these situations.

Causes

1 Cardiac failure.
2 Renal failure.
(a) Acute renal failure with oliguria.
(b) Chronic renal failure.
3 Nephrotic syndrome.
4 Hepatic insufficiency.
5 Trauma.
Except in renal failure, urine Na is usually less than 10 mmol l^{-1}.

Cardiac failure

As cardiac failure worsens, decompensation occurs with a fall in cardiac output. This results in a reduced distending pressure within the systemic arterial vasculature, which is perceived as a reduction in effective arterial blood volume. Such a patient behaves as though he were volume depleted and retains salt and water avidly, due to the following mechanisms:
(a) Reduction in renal blood flow and GFR.
(b) Increased tubular reabsorption of Na and water.
(c) Redistribution of renal blood flow.

REDUCTION IN RENAL BLOOD FLOW AND GFR

Reduction in arterial blood pressure is sensed by baroreceptors in the carotid sinus and elsewhere. This results in increased sympathetic nervous system activity which leads to peripheral and renal vasoconstriction, resulting in decreased renal blood flow. GFR is reduced proportionately rather less because constriction affects mainly efferent arterioles. The renin angiotensin system is stimulated due to reduced effective blood volume and increased sympathetic activity. This results in increased circulating and intrarenal angiotensin II, further renal vasoconstriction and reduction in renal blood flow and GFR.

INCREASED TUBULAR REABSORPTION OF SALT AND WATER

This is the major factor in increasing Na and water retention in congestive cardiac failure. Precise mechanisms remain to be elucidated. Efferent arteriolar constriction reduces peritubular capillary hydrostatic pressure. This, in conjunction with an increase in peritubular capillary osmotic pressure, which occurs commonly in congestive cardiac failure, would enhance proximal tubular reabsorption. Micropuncture studies have demonstrated increased Na reabsorption in the loop of Henle. In addition, aldosterone secretion is increased, presumably due to stimulation by elevated levels of angiotensin II. This will enhance distal tubular Na reabsorption. Other hormones which may play a part in salt and water retention are:

Natriuretic hormone.
Catecholamines.
Prostaglandins.
Kinins.
ADH.

This aspect has been discussed more fully in Chapter 2.

REDISTRIBUTION OF INTRARENAL BLOOD FLOW

In congestive cardiac failure xenon washouts studies and autoradiographic techniques have shown a redistribution of blood flow from the superficial to the deep cortex within the kidney. Deeper cortical nephrons are said to have longer loops of Henle and a greater capacity to reabsorb Na.

MANAGEMENT

1 If cardiac output (CO) is reduced, measures should be taken to improve it; these will include:
(a) Appropriate treatment of cardiac arrythmias.
(b) Inotropes, such as digitalis, dopamine.
2 If cardiac output is normal then treatment should be directed to the underlying cause, for example:
(a) Correction of anaemia.
(b) Repair of arteriovenous fistulae.
(c) Treatment of thyrotoxicosis.

(d) Treatment of thiamine deficiency.
3   If these measures fail, salt and water restriction are appropriate.
4   Diuretics. If the cardiac failure is mild, thiazides diuretics with potassium supplements may be sufficient. In more severe degrees of congestive cardiac failure, more powerful diuretics such as frusemide (a loop diuretic) perhaps with a distally acting potassium conserving diuretic such as amiloride or spironolactone are more suitable.

Renal failure

If a patient in this group has a urine Na greater than 20 mmol l^{-1} then acute or chronic renal failure causing renal salt loss is usually the problem. Hyponatraemia may then be compounded by iatrogenic administration of intravenous dextrose. Renal disease is discussed more fully in Chapter 11.

Nephrotic syndrome

Expansion of ECF volume may be particularly marked in the nephrotic syndrome, which is characterised by severe oedema, with heavy loss of protein in the urine. This protein loss consists mainly of albumin and the resultant hypoalbuminaemia and reduction in circulating plasma volume or colloid osmotic pressure are potent stimuli for ADH production. Low plasma colloid osmotic pressure favours loss of water and salt from intravascular to interstitial compartments and hence oedema occurs. Renal retention of salt and water occurs but this is soon lost into interstitial fluid because of the persistently low plasma colloid osmotic pressure.

MANAGEMENT

Management of nephrotic syndrome consists of treating any glomerular disease, for example, using steroids in minimal lesion glomerular disease, administering a high protein diet and restricting salt and water. When diuretic therapy is started, a brisk diuresis may occur, producing a further reduction in circulating blood volume and cardiovascular collapse. Concurrent administration of albumin often enhances the diuresis. In the long standing cases large doses of a potent loop diuretic may be required.

Hepatic cirrhosis

Ascites is initiated by transudation of fluid into the peritoneal cavity from congested lymphatics on the surface of the liver. If this loss of fluid is marked, it leads to intravascular volume depletion and stimulation of the mechanisms for salt and water retention. Aldosterone secretion is raised and in severe liver impairment, its metabolism is reduced. Hypoalbuminaemia is usual in severe cirrhosis. Continuing salt and water retention is potentiated by:

1 Hepatic venous obstruction.
2 Inferior vena caval obstruction, producing a fall in venous return and cardiac output.
3 Myocardial disease due to alcohol.
4 Poor nutritional state.
5 High output cardiac failure due to abnormal vascular anastomoses within liver and lungs.

MANAGEMENT

Management is largely that of the primary liver disease and includes improvement in nutrition, with salt and water restriction.
Diuretics. Hypokalaemia is common in hepatic cirrhosis so it is important to use a potassium conserving diuretic. If potent loop diuretics are required, potassium supplements will also be necessary. If these measures fail to control ascites and paracentesis is required for the patient's comfort or to facilitate respiratory exchange, then retransfusion of this high protein fluid is a useful manoeuvre. Co-existent cardiac failure should be treated along the usual lines.

Trauma

Following trauma and surgery and in hypercatabolism, tissue breakdown occurs releasing water which will expand total body water. As this water is freely diffusible between all compartments, it will produce hyponatraemia.

Idiopathic oedema

In this situation, both salt and water retention may occur. Idiopathic oedema is a condition that occurs principally in females. Fluid retention occurs predominantly during the day while the patient is ambulant, with diuresis at night. The aetiology is uncertain but may be due to increased permeability of the capillary wall, which increases transudation of salt and water into the interstitium, producing intravascular depletion. Management includes reassurance, salt and water restriction, rest during the day and diuretics which if overused will reduce intravascular volume and perpetuate the oedema producing mechanisms.

Hyponatraemia and sick cells

In many very ill patients plasma Na is low due to widespread increase in cell membrane permeability. This results in flow of Na ions along their concentration gradient from ECF into cells and K flow in the reverse direction to increase plasma K. This hyponatraemia worsens as the patient's condition deteriorates and improves with clinical improvement. Cell membrane permeability is known to be increased by hypoxia, substrate depletion (decreased ATP), metabolic inhibitors and endotoxin.

Another possible mechanism for this hyponatraemia is the reduction in ICF osmolality which occurs in the very ill patient and results in water leaving the cell to render ECF hypoosmolar. ADH secretion results in water retention and further ECF dilution. The increased membrane permeability may allow Ca ions into hypothalmic osmoreceptors with nonspecific release of ADH. Administration of Na in the sick cell syndrome is dangerous and will further increase K loss from the cell.

In these circumstances measures which increase the activity of the Na pump may be valuable. These measures include:
1 Administration of glucose and insulin with added K depending on the plasma K concentration.
2 Steroid administration.

In these very sick patients, the circulation may be unstable and a plasma expander may be necessary. Human plasma protein fraction (HPPF) may be valuable, but unfortunately has a high Na content and salt-free albumin in these circumstances may be preferred. This subject is discussed more fully in Chapter 10.

Aspects of management of hyponatraemia have been discussed under individual categories. The presence of a low plasma Na requires more active treatment if the fall in Na is acute. Giving Na for hyponatraemia diagnosed from a pathology report is illogical and potentially dangerous. A laboratory result should *never* be treated without a full history and examination of the patient. Formulae which calculate the Na deficit should be used as guidelines only and accurate, repeated measurement of plasma and urinary electrolytes are mandatory with regular review of the clinical state of the patient. Disturbances which develop over a prolonged period seldom require acute treatment, only that directed at the underlying disease. Patients in renal failure may require dialysis to remove excess salt and water. This is discussed more fully in Chapter 11.

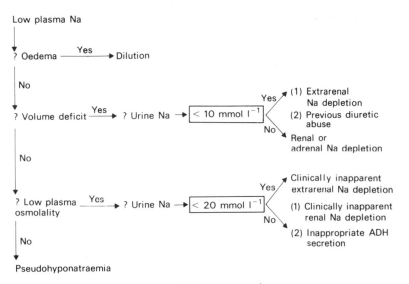

Fig. 6.1 Summary of causes of hyponatraemia.

HYPERNATRAEMIA

Definition

Plasma Na concentration greater than 140 mmol l^{-1}. Such a situation implies a deficiency of water for the total body solute. These problems have already been discussed in Chapter 5. A high oral Na intake is very unlikely to result in hypernatraemia because of intense stimulation of thirst. Patients with Cushing's syndrome and hyperaldosteronism, despite Na retention, rarely present with hypernatraemia and the accompanying hypokalaemic alkalosis suggest the diagnosis.

Excessive protein intake in the course of nasogastric feeding may increase urea production and result in osmotic diuresis. Such an osmotic diuresis induced therapeutically with mannitol or accidentally by hyperglycaemia is an important cause of hypernatraemia. Prolonged iatrogenic parenteral infusion of saline especially hypertonic NaHCO₃ may cause hypernatraemia.

In a recent study of severe hypernatraemia in adults with plasma Na greater than 154 mmol l^{-1} the commonest causes were diabetes mellitus and intracranial disorders. Diabetics may develop a hyperosmolar, nonketotic state with hypernatraemia despite treatment with hypotonic 0.45% saline. Intracranial disorders may be accompanied by abnormal production of ADH and frank DI is not uncommon. When urine Na excretion is low, infusion of 0.9% saline may make the hypernatraemia worse.

Management

This consists of encouraging oral water intake or administering 5% dextrose parenterally slowly.

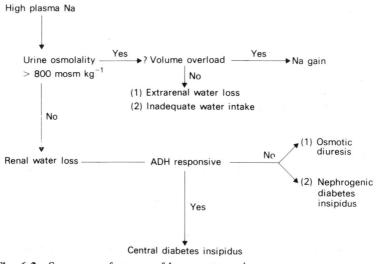

Fig. 6.2 Summary of causes of hypernatraemia.

ABNORMALITIES OF CHLORIDE BALANCE

These closely mirror disturbances of Na and occur in the same circumstances.

Hypochloraemia

Causes

Increased secretion and loss of gastric juice, for example.
in pyloric stenosis and prolonged nasogastric suction.
Increased renal excretion, diuretics.
Disorders of Na regulation — aldosteronism.
Dilution.
Actual hyponatraemia.
Increased bicarbonate retention.
Treatment is that of the underlying cause. If the plasma chloride is greater than 90 mmol l^{-1} then the loss does not need replacing. An estimate of the chloride deficit may be calculated as follows:

$$\text{Chloride deficit} = [\text{normal plasma chloride } (100 \text{ mmol } l^{-1}) - \text{measured plasma chloride}] \times 0.2 \times \text{body weight in kg}$$

This is along the lines of estimating Na deficit (see above). If a true chloride deficit exists then it should be replaced with 0.9% Na Cl.

Hyperchloraemia

Causes

Increased intake or administration.
Decreased production of bicarbonate.
Respiratory alkalosis.
Decreased excretion by the kidney unable to produce bicarbonate, for example, in renal tubular acidosis.
Dehydration.
Excessive absorption from the gastrointestinal tract following ureteroileostomies.
Treatment is again that of the underlying cause and almost always correction of the Na abnormality is of primary importance and may in itself correct the abnormality of chloride.

VALUE OF URINE SODIUM AND CHLORIDE MEASUREMENTS

A random urine urea and electrolyte estimation is valueless.

Urine sodium

Measurement of urine Na may be of value when the diagnosis is otherwise not apparent in states of:
1 Volume depletion.
2 Acute oliguria.
3 Hyponatraemia.

Volume depletion

The body is very efficient in conserving Na when intake is reduced. This is a mechanism which helps to preserve ECF volume. It is mediated by some reduction in GFR and an increase in tubular Na reabsorption. If a patient is volume depleted therefore, the virtual absence of Na in the urine indicates an extrarenal Na loss. If however, the urine does contain appreciable Na, which is a much rarer occurrence, then the diagnosis is one of renal salt wasting. It is very important in this context to ensure that the patient is not receiving diuretics or mannitol (or any other osmotic diuretic such as glucose). In addition to renal salt wasting a high Na loss will also occur in adrenal insufficiency when the tubular ability to reabsorb Na is impaired. Medullary cystic disease of the kidney results in a very severe impairment of renal salt conservation, requiring up to 15 g of NaCl daily to maintain Na balance. During the diuretic phase of acute tubular necrosis similar large losses of salt may occur.

Urine Na less than 10 mmol l^{-1} occurs in extrarenal salt loss.

Urine Na greater than 10 mmol l^{-1} occurs in renal salt wasting or adrenal insufficiency.

Acute oliguria

In an oliguric patient it is very important to distinguish between prerenal causes of oliguria and established acute tubular necrosis. In this context clinical evaluation of the patient and assessment of the state of the circulation using central venous pressure measurement are of paramount importance. In volume depletion alone urine Na should be low, but in acute tubular necrosis and some other renal disorders such as obstructive uropathy urine Na is usually greater than 35 mmol l^{-1}.

Urine Na less than 10 mmol l^{-1} implies a prerenal cause.

Urine Na greater than 35 mmol l^{-1} implies acute tubular necrosis.

Hyponatraemia

In hyponatraemia urine Na may be of value to relate dietary intake to renal loss when the patient is hypoosmolar. If urine Na is low in the presence of an unrestricted Na intake then the Na is being retained either to expand a depleted ECF or due to Na retention in oedematous states. Hyponatraemia is due to inadequate excretion of free water. If, however, urine Na is equal to or in excess of dietary intake then inappropriate ADH secretion or adrenal insufficiency are the likely diagnoses.

Urine Na less than 10 mmol l^{-1} occurs in volume depletion or oedematous states.

Urine Na equal to or greater than dietary intake occurs in inappropriate ADH secretion or adrenal insufficiency.

Urine chloride

This is of limited value in patients with metabolic alkalosis which may be due to chloride depletion. A urine chloride of less than 10 mmol l^{-1} implies that the patient should respond to administered chloride. In hyperadrenocorticism, on the other hand, renal bicarbonate reabsorption is stimulated and these patients remain alkalotic despite chloride administration because this ion is lost in the urine.

SALT AND HYPERTENSION

There is at present considerable controversy over the relation of Na intake to blood pressure and the value of Na restriction in the treatment of hypertension.

Very low Na intake occurs in the Papuan highlanders of New Guinea and other hunter gatherers (less than 30 mmol Na daily). In these groups blood pressure does not rise with age and essential hypertension is unknown.

Very high Na intakes have been given experimentally (600–800 mmol daily). These high levels can cause blood pressure to rise. Experimentally a more modest increase in Na intake by 100–200 mmol daily causes blood pressure to rise in normal volunteers and in patients with mild essential hypertension. Most populations however have a daily average Na intake of 90–120 mmol and the blood pressure rises with age. This however is not pathological. It is not possible to correlate an individual's blood pressure with either his Na intake or his urinary Na. In the past very low Na diets (10 mmol daily) such as the Kempner rice-fruit diet were shown to reduce blood pressure in a hypertensive patient. Recent studies of moderate salt restriction by not adding salt to food after cooking have shown a reduction in blood pressure with 100 mmol or less Na per day. There is however a wide variation in response. It may be therefore that dietary exposure to a high Na intake is an important factor in the development of essential hypertension in susceptible individuals. In this context it would be of value if the Na content of foodstuffs was printed on the wrapper. Some recent evidence suggests that the rise in blood pressure in essential hypertension is due to an increase in circulating sodium transport inhibitor. It is likely in man that the primary abnormality in essential hypertension is in the kidney. Sodium excretion is impaired resulting in expansion of ECF volume. This is continuously being corrected by an increase in a circulating substance that increases Na excretion by inhibiting tubular reabsorption of Na. This keeps ECF volume within normal limits. However the increased concentration of circulating Na transport inhibitor might increase the tone in arterioles and thereby increase blood pressure.

Many of the drugs used to treat hypertension have an effect on Na balance. Thiazide diuretics among other actions increase urinary Na excretion. With the notable exception of beta-adrenergic blocking drugs many antihypertensive agents increase plasma renin. The thiazide derivative, diazoxide in addition to producing hyperglycaemia has been shown to produce Na retention by this effect on plasma renin.

Angiotensin II is the most potent vasoconstricting agent known to occur naturally in man. Angiotensin II is an octapeptide formed by the action of converting enzyme on angiotensin I, and this in turn is formed from its precursor by the action of renin on angiotensinogen. In addition to the vasoconstrictor effects of angiotensin II it also releases aldosterone with characteristic effects on Na retention. Angiotensin production may be interrupted at various stages in its pathway.

1 Saralasin is a competitive antagonist of angiotensin II which can be administered intravenously. In a hypertensive patient who normally has a high level of circulating renin, saralasin infusion will produce a reduction in blood pressure. Experimentally in normal subjects infusion of saralasin produces no changes in aldosterone, angiotensin II or blood pressure but after Na depletion saralasin infusion causes a fall in aldosterone. This confirms the role of the renin angiotensin system in increasing aldosterone secretion during Na depletion.

2 Converting enzyme inhibitors.

Captopril inhibits angiotensin I converting enzyme. The effect of this is a reduction in angiotensin II and aldosterone but an increase in renin and angiotensin I. Administration of captopril results in a fall in blood pressure proportional to the pretreatment renin concentration. Other factors such as increased survival of bradykinin or increased production of prostaglandins may also contribute to the hypotensive action. The fall in aldosterone results in excretion of Na but this effect is offset by these effects:

(a) Reduction in the direct natriuretic action of angiotensin II.

(b) Reduced natriuresis due to blood pressure reduction.

Plasma K rises which may be due to the reduction in aldosterone. At present the use of captopril is reserved for the treatment of otherwise refractory hypertension especially in patients with renovascular hypertension. The drug has exhibited some side effects which may be serious such as agranulocytosis and Guillain Barré syndrome so it is clearly not a drug for first line therapy. Whenever therapy with captopril is undertaken plasma Na and K must be monitored regularly. Hyponatraemia had been reported during treatment of congestive cardiac failure. One possible mechanism for this is the reduction in aldosterone.

Dopamine behaves as an intrarenal hormone. A low salt diet (20 mmol) is associated with a low level of dopamine in the urine and with salt loading urine dopamine rises. In hypertension this rise in urine dopamine (and therefore increased natriuresis) does not occur. This may be the cause or a consequence of hypertension but it may lead to either inappropriate vasoconstriction or inefficient Na excretion, both of which may increase arterial blood pressure.

SODIUM AND THE PREMENSTRUAL SYNDROME

Symptoms are probably due to Na and water retention due to aldosterone in the premenstrual phase. In the postovulatory phase progesterone exerts a natriuretic effect. Treatment should be directed at correcting these effects.

Chapter 7
Abnormal Potassium Balance

It has already been stated that total body K can be considerably depleted before a reduction in plasma K occurs (see Chapter 3). Plasma K is affected by pH and its correction. A fall in pH of 0.1 unit may be expected to increase plasma K by 0.4 1.5 mmol l^{-1}. Plasma K is therefore a poor guide to total body K or intracellular K. However plasma K is regulated by exchange between cells and ECF as well as renal excretion, so that changes in the concentration of ECF K can to some extent be buffered by uptake or release of K from cells.

HYPOKALAEMIA

Definition

A reduction in plasma K to less than 3.5 mmol l^{-1}.

This level varies a little between laboratories. People on a normal diet take in approximately 80 mmol K daily so that deficiency due to reduced intake is rare and most cases are due to increased losses although tube feeding or parenteral nutrition with inadequate K supplementation may result in hypokalaemia. Occasionally in the elderly with a very poor diet K supplements may be indicated. The K concentrations in gastrointestinal secretions are given in Table A.4 (see p. 85).

Causes of hypokalaemia

Gastrointestinal losses

Vomiting or nasogastric suction.
Malabsorption.
Diarrhoea.
Laxative abuse.
Ureterosigmoidostomy.
Fistulae.
Villous papilloma of the rectum.
Ion exchange resins.

Renal losses

Hyperaldosteronism.
Diuretic therapy.
Steroid therapy, Cushing's disease.
Ectopic ACTH syndrome.
Liquorice, carbenoxolone.
Excessive renin secretion.
Congestive cardiac failure (CCF).
Nephrotic syndrome.
Cirrhosis.
Liver failure.
Bartter's syndrome.
Renal tubular acidosis.
Diuretic phase of acute renal failure.
Post obstructive diuresis.
Uncontrolled diabetes mellitus.

Other

Alkalosis.
Insulin induced hypoglycaemia.
Periodic paralysis — familial, thyrotoxic.
Overhydration.
Amphotericin, Carbenicillin.
Severe megaloblastic anaemia.
Cardipulmonary bypass. Hypokalaemia is partly due to preoperative treatment with diuretics, and partly to hypothermia, uptake of K into cells with glucose, internal redistribution and urine loss.
Inappropriate ADH. In a recent series of the syndrome of inappropriate ADH secretion due to bronchogenic carcinoma there was little change in plasma K unless additional factors were operative.

Despite the fact that diuretics are often given with K supplements these are often inadequate to prevent hypokalaemia. This is especially likely with the powerful loop diuretics such as frusemide and ethacrynic acid. Diuretic treatment of uncomplicated hypertension is said not to be associated with significant hypokalaemia, but only a small reduction of 5–10% (or about 200 mmol) in total body K.

However, it is wise to measure plasma K at the onset of treatment and occasionally thereafter. Long term diuretics may produce a modest fall in plasma K but this is not usually associated with a fall in total body K content, red blood cell K or exchangeable K. In some situations of severe underlying disease such as CCF when secondary hyperaldesteronism may occur, K depletion may be present.

Hypokalaemia has also been reported in respiratory insufficiency with a fall in exchangeable K of 16–37%. The discharge from villous papilloma of the rectum may have a K concentration as high as 50 mmol l⁻¹.

Signs and symptoms of K depletion

Muscle weakness — this affects both smooth and skeletal muscle
    — leading to cramps and paralytic ileus.
Loss of tendon reflexes.
Fatigue.
Apathy, sleepiness.
Tachycardia.
Hypotension, postural hypotension.
Mental abnormality, confusional state.
Cardiac arrythmia, cardiac arrest.
Increased sensitivity to digitalis.

K and digitalis compete for myocardial binding sites so that hypokalaemia increases digitalis binding in the heart with symptoms of toxicity.

Hypokalaemic nephropathy occurs and the kidney is unable to excrete a concentrated urine. This leads to polyuria and nocturia.

In a complex clinical situation K losses should always be measured. 24 hour collections of urine, diarrhoea and other gastrointestinal losses from fistulae, nasogastric suction and other drainage should be made especially if these losses exceed 100 ml daily. The ECG may be some guide to the severity of K losses and must certainly be monitored during acute intravenous K replacement. ECG signs of hypokalaemia include a reduction in the height of the T wave, depression of the ST segment and occasional inversion of T waves. In severe cases a U wave appears, the QT interval and QRS complex are widened.

In almost all K losing states coexistent metabolic alkalosis occurs. Some quantitative measure of hypokalaemia is gained from plasma

HCO_3 which is increased due to accumulation of H ions inside the K depleted cells. Logically therefore K should be replaced as the chloride salt. In an acute intensive care situation a variable blood sugar and unknown renal function make manipulation of plasma K unpredictable and potentially hazardous.

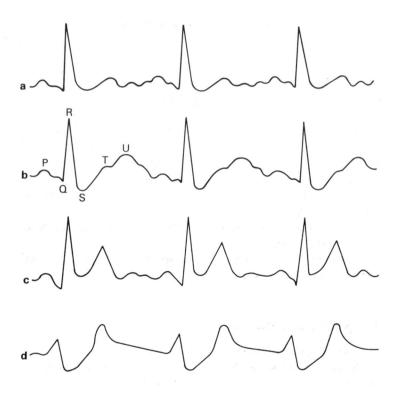

Fig. 7.1 The ECG in abnormalities of potassium. a, Normal ECG; b, hypokalaemia; c, hyperkalaemia; d, severe hyperkalaemia.

Estimation of potassium deficit

Since most of the K lost from the body is from ICF the loss occurs from a volume about twice ECF volume or about 40% body weight.

K deficit = (normal K − measured K) × 0.4 body weight (kg)

For example in a 60 kg female with plasma K 2 mmol l^{-1}:

$$K \text{ deficit} = (4.5 - 2.0) \times 0.4 \times 60$$
$$= 2.5 \times 24$$
$$= 60 \text{ mmol}$$

Treatment of hypokalaemia

A decision must first be made as to when replacement becomes necessary. When plasma K is less than 3.0 mmol l^{-1} symptoms such as cardiac arrythmia, digitalis toxicity, myopathy and nephropathy are likely and treatment is required. There is little evidence that the usual degree of hypokalaemia produced by diuretics (3.0–3.5 mmol l^{-1}) is harmful.

Therefore K should be given to increase plasma K to greater than 3.0 mmol l^{-1} and to protect patients at special risk, such as the following:
1   Those with severe heart disease on large doses of diuretics.
2   Those on digoxin.
3   Those with severe liver disease since hypokalaemia can precipitate encephalopathy.
4   Those receiving other drugs causing K loss such as corticosteroids or carbenoxolone.

Oral potassium replacement

The following preparations are available:
1   Potassium chloride (KCl). The original formulation lead to gastrointestinal ulceration.
2   Enteric coated tablets were subsequently introduced but these are still ocasionally associated with small bowel haemorrhage and ulceration.
3   Slow release K (Slow K) tablets.
4   Effervescent K.
5   KCl liquid (Kay Cee L). This is unpalatable unless given through a nasogastric tube, though very useful for rapid correction of hypokalaemia. It is rapidly absorbed from the stomach.

The usual daily dose of K is 24–63 mmol, but up to 80 mmol may be required daily in severe cases.

COMBINED TABLETS

Some manufacturers now produce a combined diuretic with K supplement in a single tablet. Usually the K content is relatively low (8 mmol) and may be quite insufficient for replacement purposes. Patients prefer such combined tablets for convenience and they do ensure that at least some K is taken with the diuretic.

HAZARDS OF ORAL K REPLACEMENT

1 Hyperkalaemia. K supplements in renal failure can produce dangerous hyperkalaemia. This can sometimes also be the case with K conserving diuretics such as amiloride used in the presence of impaired renal function.
2 Anorexia and occasionally vomiting occur.
3 Infrequently small bowel haemorrhage, ulceration (enteric coated) and stricture formation occur.
4 Slow K has produced oesophageal ulceration.
If K is required as a supplement to diuretics then a K conserving diuretic may be more appropriate for example spironolactone or amiloride.

WHO/UNICEF oral rehydration solutions have been mentioned already. There have been reports of hyperkalaemia following their use in children under one year of age. Hypernatraemia may also occur and it is recommended that these solutions are not used for longer than 24 hours without plasma electrolyte measurement.

Intravenous potassium

Again KCl is the drug of choice. Intravenous (i.v.) K is hazardous. Generally infusion should not exceed 10 mmol hour^{-1} or 120 mmol daily.

In cases of severe depletion maximum infusion of 30 mmol hour^{-1} for 1–2 hours only is permissible. K is usually added to an i.v. infusion in a concentration of 40 mmol l^{-1}. It should never be added to blood, blood products, mannitol or solutions of amino acids or lipids because it may cause lysis of red cells or may precipitate substances from solution.

If K is added to fluid in plastic containers it must be very well mixed otherwise it remains concentrated at the site of addition to the solution with potentially fatal consequences. Frequent blood samples should be taken for evaluation of K status and monitoring further therapy. If ECG signs of T wave peaking appear then the infusion should be stopped or slowed.

Intraperitoneal administration

If peritoneal dialysis is being undertaken for acute renal failure it is likely that plasma K will be high and therefore the dialysis fluid should have a low K content. Both 61 and 62 dialysates contain 0.26 g KCl per litre. Peritoneal dialysis may rarely be used for severe refractory CCF to remove excess oedema fluid and then additional K may be added to the dialysate to maintain plasma K. This is of particular importance when the patient is taking digitalis and large doses of diuretics.

Other measures to reduce potassium loss

1 During treatment of hypertension small doses of diuretic should be used. Bendrofluazide 5 mg is often an adequate dose.
2 In mild heart failure a small dose of a loop diuretic produces less K loss than a thiazide diuretic for the same fluid loss. If larger doses are required volume depletion should be avoided since this will increase aldosterone production with further K loss.
3 A moderate reduction in salt intake (70–80 mmol daily) reduces K loss by two mechanisms:
(a) It reduces the dose of diuretic required.
(b) K secretion in the distal renal tubule depends on the amount of Na delivered to this site.

Potassium chloride is one of the most frequently prescribed drugs in medical practice but should be used with great care. An American physician in 1973 argued that more lives were lost by potassium therapy than saved by it.

In hypokalaemic patients a deficit of magnesium is a very likely clinical accompaniment.

HYPERKALAEMIA

This is defined as that K concentration which exceeds the upper limit of the normal range for that reporting laboratory which effectively us usually greater than 5.5 mmol l⁻¹. Acute hyperkalaemia is a medical emergency requiring prompt recognition and treatment. Therefore it is important to rule out artifacts producing a falsely raised plasma K.

Causes of hyperkalaemia

These fall into four groups:
1 Spurious.
2 Increased intake.
3 Reduced excretion.
4 Redistribution of K, release from cells.

Spurious

Haemolysis.
Thrombocytosis.
Massive leukocytosis.
Muscle exercise during venous occlusion.

Increased intake

Iatrogenic, very rapid i.v. load.
Excess oral intake.
Several drugs such as penicillin salts and proprietary cough medicines contain large amounts of K but rarely produce severe toxicity. Salt substitutes for patients requiring low salt diets often contain considerable quantities of K. This may be of significance in cases of mild to moderate renal failure. The remarks on oral rehydrating solutions are relevant here.

Reduced excretion

This is by far the most important cause of hyperkalaemia occurring in:
Acute renal failure.
Severe chronic renal failure.
Sodium depletion.
Steroid deficiency:
Addison's disease
hypoaldosteronism.

Inappropriate use of K conserving diuretics such as Triampterene, spironolactone, amiloride.

The kidney has a very large reserve for K excretion and hyperkalaemia is uncommon until over 90% of renal function is lost and GFR is less than 20 ml min^{-1}. Both Addison's disease and isolated hypoaldosteronism can present with severe hyperkalaemia. In the latter condition there is a normal glucocorticoid response to ACTH.

Redistribution of K, release from cells

Acidosis, diabetic ketoacidosis.
Muscle injury, catabolism.
Suxamethonium.
Leukaemia chemotherapy.
Hyperkalaemic periodic paralysis.
Pathological haemolysis:
   incompatible blood transfusion
   autoimmune states
   disseminated intravascular coagulation
   malaria (falciparum)
   sodium chlorate poisoning.
Malignant hyperthermia.

Acidosis is at its worst following cardiac arrest. When extensive muscle damage occurs for example in crush injury then plasma K may rise much faster than excretion or redistribution can cope with the rise. The depolarising muscle relaxant drug suxamethonium produces fasciculation of muscle prior to paralysis. This results in an abrupt rise in plasma K especially in patients with catabolic illness, burns, muscle trauma, spinal cord injury and renal failure. Prior administration of a nondepolarising muscle relaxant such as curare, can obtund this response.

Excessive cell breakdown due to any cause will produce hyperkalaemia but K stores in the body remain normal or low.

Signs and symptoms of hyperkalaemia

Most patients are asymptomatic until there is a marked rise in plasma K (greater than 6 mmol l^{-1}) when the following symptoms develop:

Muscle weakness, loss of tendon reflexes and rarely paralysis.

Listlessness

Mental confusion.

Tingling, numbness and paraesthesia, particularly affecting the circumoral region, and the lower limbs.

Nausea, vomiting and occasionally ileus.

The ECG is the best indicator of hyperkalaemia.

ECG signs of hyperkalaemia

1   Tall tented T waves.
2   Wide QRS.
3   Widening PR.

Cardiac arrest may occur (in asystole) at plasma K levels greater than 7 mmol l^{-1}.

Hyperkalaemia is never a diagnosis made clinically and it can be seen that many of the symptoms are identical with those of hypokalaemia. However, it does much more harm than hypokalaemia although children and those with chronic impairment of renal function tolerate hyperkalaemia better than previously normal adults.

Management

The first priority is make the diagnosis by measurement of plasma K or by looking for characteristic ECG abnormalities. These however give no indication of whether the abnormality is one of excess total body K for example in renal failure or maldistribution of K which may be associated with significant total body K depletion such as occurs in severe catabolism.

Immediate treatment

Severe hyperkalaemia requires correction within minutes therefore measures to increase urinary excretion are inappropriate as they are too slow and redistribution of K is the best way of dealing with hyperkalaemia together with counteraction of the cardiac effects with calcium.

1   Intravenous calcium chloride or gluconate (5 mmol) will antagonise the cardiotoxic effects of hyperkalaemia. This dose may need to be repeated and continuous ECG monitoring is mandatory.

2   50 g glucose i.v. with soluble insulin 25 units will increase K

uptake into cells along with glucose facilitated by insulin. When insulin is used with glucose it is important to rule out Addison's disease beforehand as dangerous hypoglycaemia may occur.

3 $NaHCO_3$ 50 ml 8.4% may be given initially. This is hypertonic and should be given into a large vein. It corrects acidosis and returns K to the ICF although it must be remembered that a sodium load may be dangerous in renal failure.

Intermediate treatment

If renal failure is present any body fluid volume deficits should be corrected. Sepsis should be treated urgently and attempts made to provide adequate nutrition to reverse hypercatabolism.

Dialysis

Both haemodialysis and peritoneal dialysis will readily reduce plasma K and correct acidosis.

Ion exchange resins

Resonium A (sodium resin) or calcium resin are available. These may be given orally or rectally. Enemas should be retained for at least 30 minutes to permit exchange.

CHRONIC HYPERKALAEMIA

These situations are in the main related to renal failure where dialysis and transplantation are employed in management. Otherwise restriction of dietary protein and K, prevention of acidosis and sepsis and correction of fluid depletion are all important.

Careless administration of K supplements and K conserving diuretics should be avoided. 9–fludrocortisone (a mineralocorticoid) corrects isolated hypoaldosteronism and Addison's disease responds to glucocorticoid replacement.

During acute treatment regular measurement of plasma K concentration and continuous ECG monitoring are *mandatory* as a swing to hypokalaemia is not uncommon. This situation used to be seen during treatment of diabetic ketoacidosis with large doses of insulin.

VALUE OF URINE POTASSIUM MEASUREMENT

This may be helpful in assessment of patients with hypokalaemia and to evaluate the route of K loss. If hypokalaemia is due to K deficit then a urine K greater than 10 mmol l^{-1} suggests that the kidney is responsible for the loss unless there has been insufficient time for renal conservation to take place. Such a situation may occur in diuretic administration, metabolic acidosis or alkalosis, some renal tubular diseases, hyperadrenocorticism and occasionally in leukaemia and carbenicillin administration. If urine K is less than 10 mmol l^{-1} then the gastrointestinal tract is the likely source of K loss. Estimation of urine potassium will also be a guide to the severity of catabolism and the stress response to trauma. Postoperatively urine K losses may be very high. It is equally important however to measure other sources of K loss for example the K content of fistula losses as a guide to replacement, and always to bear in mind the effect of acid-base status on K balance.

Chapter 8
Abnormal Calcium,
Phosphate and Magnesium Balance

CALCIUM

The absolute value of plasma Ca varies with pH and albumin concentration; a low plasma albumin reduces the amount of bound Ca and hence results in a low plasma Ca (see Chapter 4).

Hypercalcaemia

Definition

Total plasma Ca greater than 2.55 mmol l^{-1}.

Causes

1 Malignancy.
2 Primary hyperparathyroidism.
3 Other causes:

vitamin D intoxication	sarcoidosis
pulmonary tuberculosis	acute renal failure
thiazide diuretics	berylliosis
tertiary hyperparathyroidism	vitamin A intoxication
hyperthyroidism	idiopathic hypercalcaemia of
immobilisation	infancy.
acromegaly	
phaeochromocytoma	

Addisonian crisis and the milk alkali syndrome are rare causes of hypercalcaemia as is familial hypocalciuric hypercalcaemia in which daily urinary Ca excretion is less than 5 mmol.

It is important to exclude false hypercalcaemia due to venous stasis, the nonfasting state and polycythaemia.

MALIGNANCY

This is the commonest cause of hypercalcaemia forming 50% of all cases.

1 Many primary tumours metastasise to bone causing bone destruction and release of Ca into the plasma. Commonest of these is carcinoma of the breast. Multiple myeloma produces a similar picture.

2 Tumours may release a hormone with parathormone like activity. The commonest tumours with this effect are carcinoma of the bronchus and hypernephroma.

PRIMARY HYPERPARATHYROIDISM

30% of newly diagnosed cases of hypercalcaemia are due to primary hyperparathyroidism (HPT) and some 20% of these have renal calculi. 77% of cases are due to parathyroid adenoma, 19% to hyperplasia and 4% to carcinoma. Now that many patients have a plasma Ca measured on a multichannel analyser more cases of hypercalcaemia are being detected. Many of these cases have only a mild increase in Ca concentration. 57% of patients in a recent series presented as a chance finding. Most at risk appear to be females over 70 years of age. 14% presented with a hypercalcaemic syndrome of dehydration and confusion (see below). In some circumstances plasma Ca may be raised only intermittently. These can be identified by a Ca tolerance test.

Calcium tolerance test. 1 g of Ca is given orally. In HPT there is hyperabsorption of Ca, marked hypercalcaemia and hypercalciuria. In addition plasma $1,25(OH)_2D_3$ levels are raised and there is abnormal suppression of PTH.

The hydrocortisone suppression test suppresses the increase in Ca due to nonparathyroid malignant disease and HPT with bone disease but not that due to HPT without bone disease. A definitive diagnosis of HPT may be made from an increase in immunoreactive PTH in the plasma of a hypercalcaemic patient but this is not readily available in Britain. The diagnosis of HPT can be made on biochemical criteria however.

Biochemical features of hyperparathyroidism
1 Raised plasma Ca.

2 Decreased renal tubular reabsorption of PO_4.
3 Increased renal tubular reabsorption of Ca.
4 Increased Ca absorption from the intestine.
5 Raised plasma $1,25(OH)_2D_3$.
6 Increased urine hydroxyproline excretion.
7 Increased plasma levels of bone alkaline phosphatase.

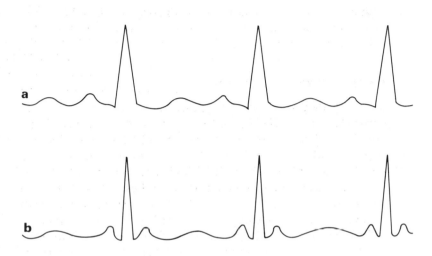

Fig. 8.1 ECG changes due to a abnormal plasma calcium. Moderate to severe hypercalcaemia shortens the QT interval on the ECG and increases susceptibility to digitalis induced arrythmia. Heart block occasionally develops. Severe hypercalcaemia leads to merging of the S and T waves and eventually cardiac arrest. a, hypocalcemia; b, hypercalcemia.

Signs and symptoms of hypercalcaemia
    Anorexia, nausea and vomiting.
    Weight loss.
    Peptic ulcer, abdominal pain.
    Constipation.
    Pancreatitis.
    Renal concentrating defect.
    Renal calculi.
    Tiredness, muscle weakness, neuromuscular paralysis.
    Cardiac arrythmias.

Ectopic calcification — cornea, conjunctiva, skin. Nephrocalcinosis and adrenal calcification occur.

Bone and joint pain.

Other symptoms of hypercalcaemia include headache. paraesthesia, apathy, mental disturbances and amenorrhoea.

Vomiting further impairs electrolyte balance and worsens dehydration.

The renal concentrating defect produces polyuria, polydipsia and
dehydration.

The kidney can excrete large amounts of Ca but renal function
becomes impaired because of the deleterious effects of hypercalcaemia on all parts of the nephron.

Effects of hypercalcaemia on the kidney

1   Reduced GFR due to renal vasoconstriction.
2   Salt loss due to inhibition of active reabsorption in the distal
tubule.
3   Water loss due to antagonism of the action of ADH on the
collecting duct.
4   Volume depletion increases proximal reabsorption of Na and
Ca thereby perpetuating and worsening the existing hypercalcaemia.

Management of hypercalcaemia

Severe hypercalcaemia is a medical emergency associated with
decreasing renal function. Treatment should be directed at the
underlying cause but if severe hypercalcaemia is present urgent
therapy should be started without awaiting the underlying diagnosis.

CORRECTION OF DEHYDRATION AND OTHER
ELECTROLYTE ABNORMALITIES

The patient may be very dehydrated at presentation but although
large volumes of fluid may be required it is important to bear in
mind that in elderly patients there is a risk of coexisting cardiac and
renal disease and that cardiac failure may be precipitated by overenthusiastic fluid loads.

FORCED SODIUM DIURESIS

This has been advocated to increase GFR and reduce renal tubular reabsorption of Ca. 4–6 litres of 0.9% sodium chloride are given daily with 20–40 mg i.v. frusemide every 4–8 hours. Frusemide further increases the loss of Ca. This technique requires very careful monitoring because of the increased urinary loss of salt and water. Urine electrolyte measurements are particularly important since large losses occur and plasma K and Mg may be reduced to dangerously low levels. In severe hypercalcaemia bone is the usual source of Ca and the next logical step is to suppress bone resorption with phosphate.

PHOSPHATE

This increases the movement of Ca into bone but some extra skeletal Ca deposits may also occur especially in overtreatment. The risks are less when phosphate is given orally for example as effervescent tablets. A suitable dose is 0.5–1.5 g neutral phosphate daily. If the patient is in coma then 50 mmol phosphate may be given i.v. over 6–8 hours. Plasma Ca may begin to fall within minutes and the effect may last several hours after the end of the infusion. A maximum of 100 mmol daily should be given.

Dangers
1   Metastatic calcification.
2   Hypocalcaemia.
3   Hypotension.
4   Oliguric renal failure.
These are reduced by limiting the plasma phosphate level to 2 mmol l^{-1}.

CALCITONIN

This suppresses bone formation with relatively little toxicity.
Three forms are available:
1   Porcine.
2   Human.
3   Salmon.

Dose. 4 MRC units kg^{-1} intramuscularly 12 hourly or in an adult 100 MRC units 12 hourly. 20% of cases fail to respond and reductions of more than 0.7 mmol l^{-1} are rare. Use of non-human calcitonin results in development of antibodies in 50% of patients which often causes resistance to treatment.

STEROIDS

These reduce intestinal absorption of Ca. The hypercalcaemia of sarcoidosis and Vitamin D intoxication respond as do some cases of malignant disease. Effects however may be slow in onset.

MITHRAMYCIN

Mithramycin should be used in a dose of 25μg kg^{-1} intramuscularly or by i.v. infusion. This should be repeated after 24–48 hours once only if the first dose is ineffective. This form of treatment is often very effective *but* with continued treatment marrow depression, renal and hepatic damage may occur.

    Intravenous chelating agents are not used nowadays.

DIALYSIS

This is a short term manoeuvre to buy time for other measures to take effect. It will also be useful if acute renal failure has already occurred or in the presence of CCF.

CIMETIDINE

This has recently been added to the treatment of HPT to reduce gastric acidity.

    Hypercalcaemia of malignant disease is often difficult to treat; steroids and a high fluid intake are the mainstays of therapy.

Surgery

Surgery is indicated in HPT for:
1 Osteitis fibrosa.
2 Recurrent renal stones.
3 Hypertension, reduced renal function.
4 Peptic ulceration.

5 Pancreatitis.

6 Psychiatric disturbance.

Mild cases of HPT may not require treatment but there is currently no way of predicting which of them will develop hypertension or renal damage. It is said that hypercalcaemic patients identified by screening have a much lower prevalence of stones than those seen before screening. If such patients are hypertensive treatment with a beta adrenergic blocking drug may reduce both the blood pressure and the PTH level thus reducing hypercalcaemia. Thiazides however will increase plasma Ca with adverse consequences.

Renal calculi

80% of renal calculi in Britain are made up of calcium oxalate or phosphate or both. Recurrent renal calculi are commonest with underlying conditions such as the following:

1 Hypercalciuria.

2 Medullary sponge kidney.

3 Renal tubular acidosis.

4 Primary hyperoxaluria.

Two forms of the condition previously called idiopathic hypercalciuria exist:

(a) Absorptive hypercalciuria.

(b) Renal hypercalciuria.

In absorptive hypercalciuria the primary abnormality seems to be increased intestinal absorption of Ca since parathyroid function is normal or suppressed and vitamin D is not concerned. In renal hypercalciuria fasting hypercalciuria exists with parathyroid stimulation in the presence of normocalcaemia. PTH stimulates renal $1,25(OH)_2D_3$ production with increased intestinal absorption of Ca.

Urinary Ca excretion may be reduced by inorganic phosphate. Sodium cellulose phosphate will bind Ca in the intestine. Thiazide administration also reduces hypercalciuria. Treatment should be continued indefinitely. Therapy should also be directed at the other underlying causes of recurrent renal calculi.

Hypocalcaemia

Definition

This occurs when the total plasma Ca is less than 2.20 mmol l^{-1}.

Causes

1 Hyperthyroidism. This may be primary, idiopathic or secondary to accidental removal of the parathyroid glands at thyroidectomy.
2 Pseudohypoparathyroidism.
3 Magnesium deficiency, usually following extensive resection of the intestine or prolonged parenteral nutrition without adequate supplements (see Chapter 12).
4 Vitamin D deficiency.
(a) Reduced oral intake or absorption; Vitamin D_3 is formed by the action of sunlight on ergosterol in the skin and D_2 is found in foodstuffs such as oily fish, margarine, eggs and milk concentrates. To develop vitamin D deficiency therefore one has to be deficient in both dietary sources and sunlight. This tends to occur in Asian immigrants of all ages and in the elderly confined to home.
(b) Disturbed metabolism. The metabolism of vitamin D is discussed in Chapter 4. In advanced renal failure there is a reduction in $1,25(OH)_2D_3$ production and this is a major factor in the development of renal osteodystrophy. Some drugs such as phenytoin act as hepatic enzyme inducers and by induction of the hepatic microsomal P450 system speed the turnover of vitamin D facilitating production of less active metabolites thereby reducing its effects and resulting in osteomalacia.
5 Renal failure.
6 Other causes of hypocalcaemia include acute pancreatitis, sodium citrate or EDTA administration, osteoblastic secondary bone deposits and malignancy treated with cytotoxic agents. Infants receiving cows milk derivatives with a high phosphate content may become hypocalcaemic. Massive infections of subcutaneous tissues, burns during slough and early granulation and generalised peritonitis produce hypocalcaemia because large amounts of Ca are immobilised in the diseased tissues and exudates. In septic shock a lowered ionised Ca concentration occurs which is correlated with a reduction in cardiac output. Any surgical operation may produce transient hypocalcaemia. Hypoalbuminaemia reduces bound Ca only.

MYASTHENIC STATES ASSOCIATED WITH IONIC IMBALANCE

Most often these are due to acute shifts or losses of K but severe Ca depletion may produce similar acute muscle weakness because of the loss of the calcium facilitating effect on acetylcholine release. Administration of magnesium has a similar effect on neuromuscular transmission to that of Ca depletion.

Signs and symptoms of hypocalcaemia

NEUROMUSCULAR FUNCTION

Neuromuscular function is severely impaired with paraesthesiae, muscle cramps and tetany.

TETANY

This is a spasm of muscle from any cause usually a low *ionised* Ca due to hypocalcaemia or severe alkosis from overbreathing or the vomiting in pyloric stenosis.

Latent tetany can be demonstrated by Trousseau's sign or Chvostck's test but if tetany is severe there may be spontaneous spasm of the muscles of the hand (*main d'accoucheur*) or carpopedal spasm. In infants laryngeal stridor occurs. Patients may present with abdominal pain due to spasm of these muscles.

OTHER FEATURES OF HYPOCALCAEMIA

Tingling, numbness, pins and needles in the hands and face are often worse after overnight fasting. Epilepsy may be the presenting feature especially in children and generalised electroencephalogram (EEG) changes may be present. Oculogyric crises and an extrapyramidal syndrome may occur.

It is classical that unless it is severe, hypocalcaemia is not diagnosed for years by which time personality changes with depression and irritability may be present.

Intracranial calcification, cataracts and systemic moniliasis occur in hypoparathyroidism.

Idiopathic hypoparathyroidism may be associated with Addison's disease. Rickets with knock knees, bow legs and a rickety rosary occurs in children and osteomalacia in adults.

Associated phosphate abnormalities are described in the next section. Magnesium deficiency should always be suspected when hypocalcaemia is diagnosed.

ECG CHANGES OF HYPOCALCAEMIA

Hypocalcaemia delays ventricular repolarisation and increases the QT interval and ST segment (see Fig. 8.1). Heart block and ventricular arrythmias may develop. The heart may be refractory to digoxin.

Treatment of hypocalcaemia

As far as possible this is treatment of the underlying cause.

CALCIUM

Oral supplements should be given in a dose of 22 mmol daily (1 g of elemental Ca). Even with oral therapy repeated plasma Ca levels should be measured.

   In acute hypocalcaemia or in situations where myocardial function is compromised treatment with intravenous Ca salts may be required. Two preparations are available:
1   Calcium gluconate.
2   Calcium chloride.
Calcium chloride has advantages: the body's retention of this salt is greater and more predictable than calcium gluconate. The positive ionotropic effect of chloride is greater than gluconate which produces an unpredictable increase in ionised Ca. Both preparations are available in 10 ml ampoules containing 5–10 mmol of Ca ($CaCl_2$) or 2.23 mmol (calcium gluconate). Administration of i.v. Ca is *dangerous* and should only be done under ECG control *slowly*. Particular care should be taken in acidotic patients or those receiving digitalis. Severe arrhythmias can occur. If i.v. Ca is to be given by continuous infusion then it must on no account be added to blood, blood products, lipid or aminoacid solutions. Up to 5 mmol 8 hourly may be given in this way. For supplementation during total parenteral nutrition about 8 mmol are required daily.

VITAMIN D

Very careful monitoring is essential to avoid overtreatment. In circumstances such as rickets where renal function is normal vitamin D_3 cholecalciferol 3000 units (75 μg) daily or 1.25 mg twice weekly will suffice. Providing renal function is normal this will be converted into $1,25(OH)_2D_3$ by the kidney and it is this metabolite which is most important for healing of vitamin D deficient rickets. However in renal osteodystrophy which was found by early workers to be resistant to vitamin D there is decreased production of $1,25(OH)_2D_3$. In addition $24,25(OH)_2D_3$ may play a part in bone formation and the level of this is depressed earlier in renal failure than $1,25(OH)_2D_3$. If this is the case both of these vitamin D metabolites will be necessary to prevent and heal renal osteodystrophy.

In hypoparathyroidism supplies of synthetic parathormone are now available but a vitamin D preparation remains the drug of choice. In the past 1–2 mg (40 000–80 000 units) vitamin D daily have been used. This therapy has a slow onset and is accompanied by hypercalcaemia sometimes prolonged. Dihydrotachysterol 0.25 mg daily and more recently $1,25(OH)_2D_3$ 1–2 μg/day has been found to control plasma Ca rapidly. Again hypercalcaemia may be a problem but it responds within days to stopping the drug.

Coexisting magnesium and potassium depletion should be corrected.

Calcium and the heart

Ca levels may be very low following massive blood transfusion as the Ca is chelated by citrate. Usually Ca is rapidly restored from the large Ca pool in the skeleton but if the blood pressure is low and perfusion poor restoration may take some time and myocardial depression occur unless intravenous Ca is given.

In the resting state cell membranes are more permeable to K than to Na ions. Depolarisation in a cardiac cell is associated with a rapid influx of Na. At a certain level of depolarisation a slow flow of Ca ions prolongs depolarisation to a plateau phase. Then the membrane becomes more permeable to K and less so to Na, repolarisation occurs and the action potential declines.

Excitation of muscle is associated with release of Ca from stores and binding of Ca to the inhibitory troponin-tropomysin complex thence antagonising its inhibitory action and muscle contraction occurs. If ECF Ca is prevented from entering the cell muscle contraction is prevented. In animals high concentrations of isoprenaline cause myocardial necrosis due to a flood of Ca ions into cells with excessive activation of Ca dependent intracellular

ATPases, energy depletion, mitochondrial damage and finally cell necrosis. This is prevented by slow channel Ca blocking drugs, for example verapamil, and beta-blocking drugs.

Calcium antogonists

Drugs which prevent passage of Ca through channels in cell membranes will have two effects:
1 They may relax muscle and produce vasodilation.
2 They may alter cardiac rhythm (effect on depolarisation).
Drugs which produce an effect by Ca antagonism:
   Verapamil.
   Nifedipine.
   Prenylamine.
   Perhexiline.
Verapamil blocks Ca flux in the atrioventricular node and is useful for treatment of supraventricular arrthymias. The ECG should be monitored continuously during intravenous administration. Nifedipine is used in the treatment of angina and hypertension. Prenylamine is used for angina but in the presence of hypokalaemia is prone to cause arrythmias. There is some recent evidence that these drugs may be of value in exercise induced asthma. This may be due to Ca dependent mediator release and Ca antagonists act by blocking Ca channels and hence reducing post exercise bronchoconstriction.

Calcitonin

Calcitonin is the drug of choice in Paget's disease. Although lack of calcitonin may be an important factor in the rapid development of bone loss after the menopause and prophylactic treatment with calcitonin may prevent this there is no evidence that such treatment can reverse established osteoporosis. If pregnancy occurs in very deprived conditions of grossly deficient Ca diets the mother's skeleton is sacrificed for the fetus and calcitonin levels are depressed. Calcitonin is therefore of great importance in controlling and reducing the rate of skeletal resorption.

PHOSPHATE

Phosphorus is ubiquitous in human metabolism and yet its disorders are infrequent and closely related to those of Ca metabolism. Because it is so widely distributed within cells dietary deficiency with enteral nutrition is almost unknown.

Hyperphosphataemia

Definition

This exists when plasma phosphate (PO_4) is greater than 1.35 mmol l^{-1}.

Causes

1 Hypoparathyroidism.
(a) Primary, idiopathic.
(b) Secondary, postsurgical.
2 Pseudohypoparathyroidism.
3 Vitamin D toxicity.
4 Renal failure. At low GFR phosphate is retained and the resulting hyperphosphataemia may itself further impair renal function. In chronic renal failure (GFR less than 20 ml min^{-1}) the hyperphosphataemia may cause renal calcification by:
(a) Increasing the plasma Ca × PO_4 product.
(b) Causing hyperparathyroidism which would suppress renal tubular function and increase acidosis. Phosphate restriction is then appropriate.
5 Acromegaly.
6 High phosphate intakes.
7 Malignancy associated with cytotoxics.
8 Severe catabolic states.
9 Acidosis.
Hyperphosphataemia is more common in infants, children and postmenopausal women.
   A raised plasma PO_4 causes little in the way of symptoms.

Clinical manifestations

1 Ectopic calcification.

(a) Corneal, conjuctival.
(b) Nephrocalcinosis.
(c) Arterial calcification.
(d) Skin calcification.
2 Secondary hyperparathyroidism may occur in renal failure.
3 Renal osteodystrophy. Specific therapy will be required in this situation.

Treatment

Treatment is that of the underlying cause and much of it appears in the section above on Ca.

Measures to reduce PO₄ in renal failure

1 Aluminium hydroxide. This binds PO_4 in the gastrointestinal tract thereby reducing absorption. It must be remembered that hypophosphataemia is also a danger and that aluminium is toxic to the central nervous system in chronic renal failure producing an encephalopathy known as dialysis dementia.
2 Renal dialysis will reduce PO_4 levels.

Relation between phosphate and acidosis

In acidosis H ion concentration is increased. This suppresses glycolysis by inhibition of phosphofructokinase. Less adenosine triphosphate (ATP) is synthesised, less inorganic phosphate is utilised and more is therefore available in the cells and plasma.

The increase in H within the cell is initially balanced by a high PO_4. Then the H is buffered in intracellular protein and PO_4 moves out of the cell to maintain the Gibbs Donnan equilibrium. The increased PO_4 outside the cell is excreted via the kidney. Acidosis also promotes PO_4 loss by exchange of H for sodium via disodium hydrogen phosphate in the renal tubules.

A rather similar situation occurs in respiratory failure with a low arterial oxygen. In these circumstances aerobic metabolism is reduced, ATP synthesis is reduced and again plasma PO_4 rises and is presented to the kidney for excretion. When the oxygen dissociation curve is shifted to the right as occurs in acidosis there is an increase in deoxygenated haemoglobin which is a very efficient buffer and enhances PO_4 loss from cells.

Hypophosphataemia

This exists when plasma PO_4 is less than 0.8 mmol l^{-1}. This situation is of much greater importance clinically than an excess of this anion because of the importance of PO_4 within the cell.

Causes

1 Primary hyperparathyroidism and ectopic parathormone production.
2 Vitamin D deficiency.
3 Renal tubular defects; congenital and acquired.
4 Hyperventilation.
5 Alkalosis.
6 Low phosphate intake.
7 Glucose and insulin.
8 Adrenaline.
9 Glucocorticoids.
10 Chronic alcoholism.
11 Haemodialysis.
12 Postoperative situations.
13 Treatment of diabetic ketoacidosis with bicarbonate.
14 Septicaemia.
15 Beri-beri.

These causes may be grouped into:
(a) Reduced intake.
(b) Increased loss.
(c) Intercompartmental shift.

Reduced PO_4 intake is unlikely under normal circumstances but is very important in a patient receiving parenteral nutrition with inadequate supplements. Absorption of PO_4 can be reduced by magnesium or aluminium salts. Increased loss via the renal tubules occurs in HPT, steroid therapy and renal tubular insufficiency. Acidosis has already been discussed. Intercompartmental shifts occur when PO_4 enters the cell with glucose during a glucose infusion. It is then utilised in glycolysis and therefore the available phosphate is reduced. Hence hypophosphataemia may present a problem in postoperative surgical patients. The hypophosphataemia is maximal on the second or third postoperative day. The subsequent reduction in 2,3-diphosphoglycerate (2,3-DPG) is accompanied by increased haemoglobin affinity for oxygen and possible tissue hypoxia. This hypophosphataemia may be due in part to a change in the maximal tubular resorption for phosphate.

Clinical and biochemical features of hypophosphataemia

Paraesthesiae, muscle weakness.
Rickets, osteomalacia.
Impaired intermediary metabolism:
    defective glycogenolysis
    defective glycolysis
    reduced intracellular ATP.
Increased purine degradation.
Rigidity of erythrocyte membranes.
Reduced erythrocyte 2,3 DPG, impaired oxygen release.
Impaired polymorphonuclear leucocyte function, reduced chemotactic, phagocytic and bactericidal activity.
Reduced renal tubular bicarbonate reabsorption.
Seizures.
Coma.

In the acutely ill patient in an intensive care unit hypophosphataemia is especially likely. If such a patient fails to breathe adequately following a period of mechanical ventilation then measurement of plasma PO_4 should be undertaken without delay.

Management of hypophosphataemia

This hinges upon recognition of circumstances in which it is likely to occur and confirmation of the diagnosis. It is very important in this respect to ensure that blood for a plasma PO_4 estimation is NOT taken when a glucose infusion is in progress.

PHOSPHATE ADMINISTRATION

PO_4 may be given orally or intravenously.
1 Orally phosphate may be administered as 0.5–1.5 g inorganic PO_4 daily.
2 Since many situations are associated with potassium depletion the appropriate intravenous replacement is K_2HPO_4. This contains 20 mmol K and 10 mmol PO_4 in 10 ml. Another solution available for use in this country is a 500 ml polyfusor containing:

Na   162 mmol l^{-1}
K   19 mmol l^{-1}
PO$_4$ 100 mmol l^{-1}

This solution however provides rather a large sodium load. Daily requirements are 0.5–0.75 mmol kg^{-1}. In the acute situation 30–50 mmol daily should be given. To replace losses in addition to daily requirements 50–100 mmol may be required over 6–12 hours and this dose should be repeated after 24 hours. Some authorities recommend as much as 50 mmol for each 1000 calories during parenteral nutrition suggesting that overspill into the urine denotes adequate replacement.

MAGNESIUM

Hypermagnesaemia

Hypermagnesaemia exists when plasma Mg is greater than 0.9 mmol l^{-1}. This is rare and occurs mainly in chronic renal failure especially if magnesium containing antacids have been used unadvertently. It may also occur during acute renal failure although during the diuretic phase Mg levels may fall below normal. Mg should be administered with caution in the presence of latent renal disease especially if repeated administration is necessary.

Causes

1   Acute and chronic renal failure.
2   Uncontrolled diabetes mellitus.
3   Adrenocortical insufficiency.
4   Metabolic acidosis.
5   Mg containing medications for example antacids, cathartics, treatment for eclampsia.
6   Spurious hypermagnesaemia due to the sample being taken with excess venous stasis.

Clinical features of hypermagnesaemia

Impaired neuromuscular activity:
  muscle weakness
  loss of deep tendon reflexes

impaired autonomic nerve transmission
increase in the excitatory threshold.
Vasodilatation leading to hypotension.
Drowsiness.
ECG changes.

Mg levels greater than 2.5 mmol l^{-1} impair atrioventricular and intraventricular conduction. ECG changes include an increase in PR interval, broadening of the QRS complex and an increase in the height of the T wave. Mg levels greater than 5 mmol l^{-1} produce muscle paralysis similar to that due to curare. The amount of acetylcholine liberated from the neuromuscular junction is reduced, the sensitivity of the end plate to acetylcholine is impaired with decreased excitability of the muscle membrane. Respiratory centre depression occurs. Mg levels greater than 8 mmol l^{-1} are associated with coma and cardiac arrest.

Treatment of hypermagnesaemia

When cardiac conduction defects occur urgent treatment is required.
1   In renal failure dialysis is the treatment of choice.
2   In an emergency situation with arrhythmia i.v. Ca may be given cautiously under ECG control in a dose of 2.5–5 mmol.
3   An enforced Na/Ca diuresis can be attempted along the lines of that described for hypercalcaemia but this must be undertaken with great care and frequent electrolyte analysis, especially if cardiac or renal function are impaired.

REGIME FOR FORCED DIURESIS

4–6 l 0.9% sodium chloride daily.
20–4 mg frusemide i.v. 4–8 hourly.
2.5–5 mmol Ca should be given every 4–8 hours in a litre of 0.9% saline.

Hypomagnesaemia

Definition

Hypomagnesaemia exists when plasma Mg is less than 0.7 mmol l^{-1}.

Causes

1 *Reduced oral intake.*
Prolonged parenteral nutrition with inadequate supplements.
2 *Gastrointestinal disturbances.*
Vomiting.
Diarrhoea.
Prolonged nasogastric suction.
Malabsorption — Mg soap formation will reduce absorption as will administration of large amounts of Ca.
Fistulae.
Protein calorie malnutrition.
Alcoholic cirrhosis.
Pancreatitis.
3 *Endocrine.*
Hyperparathyroidism, hypoparathyroidism.
Hyperaldosteronism — primary and secondary.
Hyperthyroidism.
Diabetic coma.
Inappropriate or excess ADH.
Disorders of lactation.
4 *Renal disease*
Glomerulonephritis.
Pyelonephritis.
Hydronephrosis.
Renal tubular acidosis.
5 *Alcoholism.*
6 *Other causes* include osmotic diuresis, diuretic therapy, malignant osteolytic disease and porphyria. Hypomagnesaemia may be idiopathic, familial or occur in the newborn. Spurious hypomagnesaemia occurs in haemodilution and severe hypoalbuminaemia.

Alcohol affects the tubular mechanisms essential for reabsorption of Mg and increases production of metabolic intermediates such as lactate which bind Mg. In diabetic coma Mg shows the same changes as K. It is raised initially and falls during treatment to potentially very low levels.

Clinical features

Symptoms are erratic and no well defined clinical picture exists but the following may be found with a plasma level of 0.3–0.5 mmol l^{-1} or less:

1 Nausea, vomiting and abdominal pain.
2 Neuromuscular excitability.
(a) Tetany, cramps.
(b) Paraesthesia.
3 Muscle weakness with a coarse irregular tremor.
4 Lethargy.
5 Central nervous system effects include depression, irritability, ataxia and vertigo. Personality change with anxiety may develop and later confusion, hallucinations, coma and convulsions.
6 Tachycardia may occur with either hypertension or hypotension. Cardiac arrythmias such as ventricular ectopics are not uncommon. ECG changes include ST segment depression, T wave inversion and a prolonged QT interval. There is exacerbation of digoxin toxicity.

Tetany due to low Mg may be more likely than hypocalcaemic tetany to produce convulsions. Administration of Ca in hypomagnesaemic tetany will not improve the situation until Mg concentrations are restored. Many clinical features listed here are in fact common to a number of electrolyte abnormalities and both hypokalaemia and hypocalcaemia may be associated abnormalities.

The development of symptoms depends on the plasma concentration and the ratio of this to other ions present. Mg deficiency is manifested more readily after correction of abnormalities of Na, K, Cl, Ca and acid base balance.

During total parenteral nutrition as the patient becomes anabolic and Mg requirements increase the deficiency is made worse. Mg like K is an intracellular ion so that the plasma levels poorly reflect the total body situation and considerable deficiency can occur with a normal plasma Mg. The Mg content of red blood cells correlates better with clinical signs of deficiency than plasma levels but is still unreliable. 24 hour urine excretion of Mg may be very low in deficiency states (0.5 mmol). Normally most of an administered dose of Mg is excreted but in deficiency states 40–80% is retained.

Assessment of magnesium depletion

Failure to excrete more than 70% of an administered load of 20 mmol Mg within 16 hours indicates depletion. Alternatively 0.25

mmol kg^{-1} may be given by infusion over 1–2 hours. If less than 80% is excreted within 24 hours Mg depletion exists.

Treatment of hypomagnesaemia

Magnesium sulphate is avilable in 10, 20 or 50% solution. Oral administration may produce diarrhoea although up to 70 mmol daily can usually be given safely by this route. Daily administration of 0.1–1.0 mmol kg^{-1} is a suitable dose although correction of the intracellular deficit may take 1–2 weeks. Intravenous administration is essential to supply supplements during parenteral nutrition and is also indicated in the treatment of malignant hyperthermia, digoxin intoxication and eclampsia. During parenteral nutrition 0.04 mmol kg^{-1} are required daily but up to 1.0 mmol kg^{-1} can be safely given daily and in an emergency this dose can be given over 4 hours. Oral supplements are usually adequate if hypomagnesaemia is due to excessive diuretic therapy.

It has recently been shown that in hyponatraemic patients with severe CCF on long term diuretic therapy infusin of Mg results in an increase in plasma Na level, and an increase in muscle K. This is probably mediated through an effect of Mg on membrane ATPase.

Chapter 9
The Metabolic Response
to Trauma

This may be defined as the fluid and electrolyte changes which occur following trauma or surgical operation. A number of metabolic and endocrine changes occur which have been known for many years. After trauma there is a rise in temperature which is due to an increased metabolism. These metabolic changes have been extensively studied earlier this century by Moore and Cuthbertson. Classically, the metabolic response to trauma is divided into four phases:

1 The phase of injury. This lasts 2–4 days after major trauma unless it is prolonged by sepsis, continued fluid loss or acid base disturbance, to about seven to ten days. Changes which occur are due to adrenergic and adrenocorticoid hormones and represent catabolism. The purpose of this phase is to allow flight to safety and to maintain blood volume.

2 The turning point. The effect of phase 1 hormonal activity is terminated.

3 Anabolism. This phase begins with positive nitrogen balance and an increase in muscle mass. It may last up to 5 weeks after major trauma.

4 Fat gain. This occurs over several months and involves replenishment of the fat stores that were present before injury.

Consequences of major operation or injury

1 There is direct destruction of cells in the wound.

2 There is loss of fluid into and from the damaged area.

3 Operation and injury interfere with food intake, so that the effects of starvation are added.

4 An increase in energy expenditure occurs as metabolism increases to deal with tissue destruction and repair damage.

5 Hormonal changes occur which have both defensive and restorative actions.

HORMONAL CHANGES REGULATING THE METABOLIC RESPONSE TO TRAUMA

1 Adrenaline and noradrenaline levels are raised from 24 hours up to 3 days after trauma. Potent stimuli causing secretion of these monoamines include sepsis, hypoxia, shock and fear.

2 Plasma glucogen levels are increased.

3 Anterior pituitary hormones are increased:

(a) Growth hormone.

(b) Adrenocorticotrophic hormone (ACTH). Stimulation of the hypothalamus in trauma results in increased production of corticotrophin releasing factor. Then ACTH increases circulating plasma glucocorticoids. Hyperglycaemia, glycolysis and an increase in fatty acids may occur.

4 Antidiuretic hormone (ADH). ADH levels are increased very quickly after major surgery and in uncomplicated circumstances remain elevated for two to four days. This response to trauma overrides the normal regulation of ADH by extracellular fluid osmolality and may result in inappropriate antidiuresis.

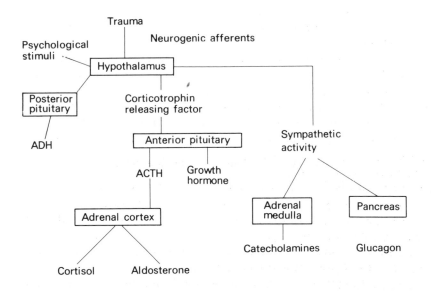

Fig. 9.1 Hormonal changes in metabolic response to trauma.

5 Aldosterone. Secretion of this hormone is raised because of an elevated ACTH. Any reduction in blood volume or extracellular fluid volume will also stimulate aldosterone release.

6 Prolactin levels rise after anaesthesia and surgery with a much greater rise in women than in men.

There are no significant alterations in thyroid hormone secretion.

FACTORS WHICH MODIFY THE EXTENT AND DURATION OF METABOLIC RESPONSE TO TRAUMA

1 Pain and analgesia.
2 Fear and sedation.
3 Post-trauma complications.
(a) Shock.
(b) Haemorrhage.
(c) Hypoxia.
(d) Sepsis.
4 Pre-existing nutritional status and debility.
5 The extent and site of the trauma.

In addition to these factors, there is a considerable individual variation in response and postoperative cortisol rise is greater in women than men. After major, uncomplicated surgery, such as gastrectomy, the energy expenditure may rise to 3500 cal daily for 4 or 5 days. The addition of sepsis may increase this expenditure to 5000 cal daily. After an uncomplicated gastrectomy weight loss may amount to about 3 kg. Half of this will be from fat and half from protein. It is interesting that in animals the normal response to trauma is to lie quite still in a warm environment. This minimises the need for increased heat production and reduces oxygen consumption and carbon dioxide production. In a more extreme situation nitrogen losses may amount to 35 g daily which corresponds to in excess of 200 g protein 1 200 g of lean tissue mass (muscle mass) daily. It has been shown that the postoperative increase in metabolic rate rises in direct relationship to the severity of the operation. An increase in energy consumption of about 10% may be expected after elective, uncomplicated surgery. This may rise to 20–50% in association with peritonitis and up to 100% after severe burns. In the absence of nutritional support, this additional energy is derived from the fat stores and increased breakdown of tissue protein. This is discussed more fully in Chapter 12 (Parenteral Nutrition). Most of the energy substrates are produced by increased lipolysis and this is reflected in the low respiratory quotient (0.7–0.8).

Insulin

After trauma insulin secretion is depressed in the acute situation for the first 72 hours. Thereafter, insulin resistance is present, often with hyperglycaemia and glycosuria and osmotic diuresis will then occur leading to dehydration. The insulin resistance is in part due to the high circulating levels of catecholamines and glucocorticoids (catabolic hormones).

These metabolic effects have a profound effect on the water, salt and potassium balance.

Water balance

An increase in ADH will produce profound antidiuresis by preventing the kidney excreting free water. Characteristically, urine volume falls and urine osmolality rises, although glomerular filtration rate will be normal if the blood volume is normal.

Endogenous water formation will be increased. Fat is broken down into free fatty acids and glycerol and muscle is broken down into its constituent amino acids; both of these are to provide energy substrates for gluconeogenesis. Oxidation of 1 kg of fat to carbon dioxide and water results in the formation of about 1 litre of water. Similar volumes of water are produced by complete oxidation of muscle protein. It is important to include this volume in the calculation of water balance postoperatively. In these circumstances this metabolic water which is released can seldom be excreted by the kidney and is retained to diffuse throughout body fluid compartments, thereby increasing total body water. This may produce hyponatraemia. Therefore the effects of fat oxidation, protein breakdown and ADH secretion result in an increase in ECF volume and haemodilution.

Salt balance

The hormonal changes which occur result in marked Na retention. Daily urine Na may fall as low as 1 mmol. Chloride retention usually accompanies this but to a slightly lesser degree. Despite this, plasma Na falls as relatively more water is retained and dilutional hyponatraemia usually occurs. If there is any degree of hypovolaemia or reduction in ECF volume, then aldosterone secretion persists and may prolong Na retention.

Potassium balance

Potassium balance parallels nitrogen balance. 70–90 mmol of K are excreted in the urine daily if no K is given. Cell breakdown is one cause of this K loss but the K to nitrogen ratio in the urine is much greater than the ratio within cells. The sick cell syndrome has already been discussed in Chapter 6. Potassium moves out of cells and Na or H ions leak into cells. Some of this K which moves out of the cells will then be excreted in the urine. The increased secretion of aldosterone will result in an increased exchange of Na for K in the renal tubules.

Normally after the seventh day these hormonal changes are reversed. Na, K and water balance return to normal. The phase of anabolism will then begin.

METHODS OF MINIMISING THE METABOLIC RESPONSE TO TRAUMA

This response can, to some extent, be obtunded by good surgical technique, with minimal tissue damage and good intraoperative management. There should be a minimum of delay between the time of trauma and medical and surgical treatment, as any delay prior to definitive treatment has a significant effect on morbidity and mortality.

1   Blood and fluid losses should be precisely replaced.
2   Perfect oxygenation should be maintained under all circumstances.
3   The patient should receive adequate nutritional support. This is further discussed in Chapter 12.

4 Adequate analgesia should be given at all times.

It has been recognised for some time that afferent sensory impulses from the injured area are important factors in precipitating these hormonal changes. Profound analgesia and a sensory blockade have been tried in an attempt to prevent the metabolic response to surgery, by extradural and spinal anaesthesia and large doses of intravenous analgesic agents. Extensive extradural analgesia may inhibit the cortisol and glucose response to lower abdominal surgery. However, it is much less effective in abolishing the metabolic response in upper abdominal and thoracic surgery. Although thoracic block of sympathetic fibres may prevent hyperglycaemia, the hormonal changes may well result from stimulation of vagal afferent fibres and therefore be unresponsive to extradural block. An alternative approach is to use large doses of intravenous morphine or the synthetic opiate, Fentanyl. Indeed, it does seem that large doses of these narcotic analgesics will abolish the cortisol, growth hormone and hyperglycaemic response to major trauma. Fentanyl and oxygen anaesthesia prevents the ADH response in patients with heart disease undergoing surgery. It is not yet clear whether obtunding the metabolic response to trauma acutely, has in fact any long term benefit on aspects such as negative nitrogen balance. Further discussion of the management of the perioperative state is referred to in Chapter 10.

Chapter 10
Fluid Balance in
the Surgical Patient

PREOPERATIVE ASSESSMENT, FLUID BALANCE AND RESUSCITATION

A patient presenting for minor or moderate elective surgery is unlikely to require preoperative fluid therapy. A patient who is already ill may have a variety of fluid and electrolyte disturbances.
1 Loss or gain of water causing disturbed osmolality.
2 Abnormal ECF volume, intravascular volume or cardiac output.
3 Disturbances in Na, Ca, K which are discussed elsewhere.

Assessment of the disorder

History

A history of fluid therapy and loss is invaluable. In the case of pyloric stenosis with vomiting for example predictable water, Na, K, Cl and H losses may occur and marked metabolic alkalosis with tetany may be present. Although an estimate of the loss of electrolyte may be made from known concentrations in different secretions wide variation does occur and measurement of the electrolyte content of losses in excess of 100 ml is essential.

FLUID BALANCE CHART

An accurate fluid balance chart is of great value in assessment of fluid requirements but except in special units it is also very difficult to find. Allowance must be made for insensible losses.

Clinical examination

A search should be made for dry mucous membranes or oedema. The pulse volume and blood pressure should be estimated and the chest examined for basal crepitations. Severe hidden fluid loss may occur in paralytic ileus.

Table 10.1 Composition of secretions.

Secretion	Na	K	Cl	HCO₃	Volume
		mmol l⁻¹			(litres 24 hour⁻¹)
Parotid					
saliva	112	19	40	–	1.5
Gastric					
juice	50	15	140	0–15	2–3
Panacreatic					
juice	130	5	55	110	0.5–1
Bile	145	5	100	38	0.5–1
Ileal juice	140	11	70	Variable	–
Normal					
stool	20–40	30–60	20	–	0.1
Diarrhoea	30–140	30–70	–	20–80	Variable
Insensible					
sweat	12	10	12	–	0.5

If visible sweating occurs there is a marked increase in its sodium and chloride concentration.

Weight

Changes in body weight of 0.5–1 kg in 24 hours are usually due to loss or gain of water. Although it is a simple matter to weigh a healthy patient daily weighing of a sick patient is surprisingly difficult. Table 10.2 relates the degree of dehydration to weight loss.

Table 10.2 Assessment of dehydration.

	Fluid loss in children (% body weight)	Fluid loss in adults (% body weight)
Mild dehydration	5	4
Moderate dehydration	10	6
Severe dehydration	15	8

Biochemical measurement

Blood urea, haemoglobin and haematocrit will rise in dehydration. When this becomes severe plasma Na will also begin to rise. In conditions of plasma loss, for example pancreatitis, a haemotocrit of 60% or over constitutes a life threatening emergency.

Urine output

A urine output of $0.5-1$ ml kg^{-1} hour^{-1} is acceptable. When an adult becomes oliguric 25 ml or less urine will be produced hourly. It is then essential to know whether this is due to hypovolaemia (reduced renal perfusion), to renal disease or to post renal obstructive factors.

OLIGURIA

Various investigations will help to elucidate the underlying cause.
1   Urine specific gravity > 1.016 suggests a prerenal cause for oliguria.
2   Urine Na > 30 mmol l^{-1} suggests intrinsic renal failure.
3   Blood urea > 35 mmol l^{-1} suggests intrinsic renal failure.
4   Urine urea < 185 mmol l^{-1} strongly suggests intrinsic renal failure.
5   Urine: plasma urea ratio. If oliguria has a prerenal cause this ratio will be $> 20:1$.
(a) In early intrinsic renal failure it will be $< 14:1$.
(b) In late intrinsic renal failure it will be $< 5:1$.
6   Urine: plasma osmolality ratio. If oliguria has a prerenal cause this will be $> 2:1$.
(a) In early intrinsic renal failure it will be $< 1.7:1$.
(b) In late intrinsic renal failure it will be $< 1.1:1$.

RESPONSE TO DIURETICS

The ability of the kidney to respond to a diuretic may be tested. 20g mannitol (100 ml 20%) is infused over 20 minutes. The absence of a diuresis implies intrinsic renal failure. In a patient who is already hypervolaemic mannitol administration may precipitate pulmonary oedema especially if it cannot be excreted. If the central venous pressure (CVP) is very high 1 g of frusemide should be given instead (see Chapter 11).

Central venous pressure

This is the pressure measured from the right atrium (RA) and it is a reflection of the volume of the circulation and the ability of the right heart myocardium to deal with the venous return. A low CVP indicates hypovolaemia either absolute or relative for example profound vasodilatation of histamine release. A high CVP suggests failure of the right heart for whatever reason. Unfortunately the CVP may be misleading in hypovolaemic states due to the intense vasoconstriction of both arterioles and capacitance vessels which increases venous return and maintains the CVP within the normal range (3–7 cm water above the right atrium).

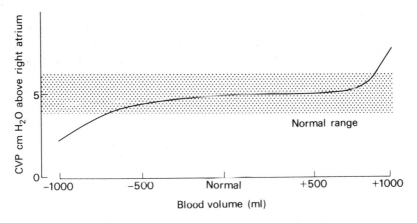

Fig. 10.1 The relationship between CVP and blood volume.

However, serial measurements of CVP are very valuable if severe loss or gain of fluid is anticipated or in elderly patients with cardiac or renal disease.

Unfortunately CVP measured in the RA does not always reflect the state of the left heart. A flotation catheter (Swan Ganz) may be necessary to measure pulmonary capillary wedge pressure (PCWP) which reflects left arterial pressure (LAP) and is normally 6–12 mmHg. This is the effective filling pressure or *preload* of the left side of the heart. When myocardial function is impaired measurement of LAP is a more useful and safer guide to blood volume replacement than CVP.

Very large volumes of fluid can be infused without a rise in CVP but with a marked increase in lung water and Na which can be very deleterious. Then a rise in LAP warns against further fluid administration and suggests that pulmonary oedema may occur. If the colloid osmotic pressure (COP) is normal pulmonary oedema occurs with a LAP of 20 mmHg or more.

Chest X-ray

The chest X-ray may show pulmonary oedema either interstitial or intra-alveolar.

Fluid losses

Normal preoperative 'nil by mouth' regimes do not usually cause significant water loss. Insensible fluid loss continues unabated and may be raised by pyrexia or high environmental temperature. Further loss may be incurred by diuretics, enemas, or vomiting due to premedication. Loss or gain of H_2O results in disturbed osmolality which can be corrected as already described in Chapter 5. Losses of isotonic saline, plasma proteins or blood cause reduction of intravascular volume and minimal change in toxicity. Such losses require urgent replacement preoperatively.

Intravascular volume, cardiac output and shock

A patient who has a reduced blood volume requires this to be replaced with the correct fluid prior to surgery, so as to maintain a stable cardiovascular system (CVS) throughout the procedure.

Shock

Shock exists when the cardiac output is inadequate to supply the nutritional demands to all tissues. In practice this involves inadequate blood flow to the tissues and results in cell damage leading to cardiac, pulmonary, metabolic, renal and microcirculatory complications. It does not necessarily mean that cardiac output is below normal.

Causes of shock

Hypovolaemic shock (heart normal)
  haemorrhage
  plasma loss, burns
  pancreatitis
  peritonitis.
Relative hypovolaemia
  septicaemia
  anaphylaxis.
Cardiogenic shock
  inadequate performance of the left ventricle (LV).

Clinical signs of hypovolaemic shock include a reduction in blood pressure (BP) and urine output, a rise in pulse rate and cold cyanosed extremities with slow capillary refill after blanching. In hypovolaemia renal blood flow shifts from the outer renal cortex to the inner juxtamedullary portions of the kidney where there are fewer glomeruli with longer loops of Henle. This shift in blood flow results in increased reabsorption of Na and water. As less filtrate is presented to the tubules the reabsorption of Na is further increased. Reduced Na concentration in the distal tubule and a reduction in perfusion pressure in the renal arterioles both stimulate the juxtaglomerlar apparatus to secrete renin. This then increases aldosterone production. Hypovolaemia or impaired perfusion also stimulates ADH release.

MANAGEMENT

Management of hypovolaemic shock includes establishing the diagnosis followed by mechanical haemostasis and treatment of the underlying condition.

With CVP and urine output monitoring fluid is infused if the CVP is low (normal CVP is 3–7 cm water above the RA) bearing in mind that the change in CVP with blood volume replacement is not linear (see Fig. 10.1). If there is doubt about the adequacy of the circulating blood volume 200 ml fluid can be infused rapidly (fluid loading test). If the CVP rises by more than 2 cm water for more than 10 minutes then no further fluid is required for the time being. If the CVP is greater than normal in shock and PCWP measured by Swan Ganz catheter is less than 12 mmHg then volume expansion is indicated. If PCWP is greater than 15 mmHg vasoactive or inotropic drugs are indicated.

The most important aspects of volume replacement are:
1 Early recognition of its necessity.
2 Rapid institution.
3 Frequent reassessment of the clinical state of the patient and revision of treatment.

FLUIDS AVAILABLE TO TREAT
HYPOVOLAEMIC SHOCK

1 Blood.
2 Plasma.
3 Dextran.
4 Gelatin.
5 Crystalloid.

BLOOD

Blood of the correct group should be used to treat haemorrhagic shock if the haemotocrit is less than 25% and should be continued until a satisfactory clinical state is achieved. The haematocrit of stored whole blood is 35% and that of packed cells is 70%. Stored blood is very unlike the patients own circulating blood. It is stored in a citrate anticoagulant with dextrose. Two such solutions are currently available:
1 Acid citrate dextrose (ACD) solution 120 ml. When this is mixed with 420 ml of blood the mixture has an initial pH of 7.4 at 4°C but this falls during storage.
2 Citrate phosphate dextrose (CPD). This has certain advantages over ACD for blood preservation. These include slightly less haemolysis, less K leak from the cells and better post-transfusion survival of red blood cells. Twenty-day-old blood stored in CPD can be expected to have a pH of 6.71. This is a higher pH than in ACD blood and correlates with a longer shelf life. Storage of blood reduces the number of red cells which survive after transfusion. 99% of red blood cells survive 24 hours post-transfusion if the blood is given immediately after collection, but only 75–80% survive 24 hours if the blood has been stored for 21 days.
2,3 Diphosphoglycerate (2,3 DPG). This is better maintained in CPD blood than in ACD blood mainly because of the greater pH of the CPD solution. Blood can be transfused up to 4 weeks after

collection if stored in CPD. 2,3 DPG is important in affecting the position of the oxygen dissociation curve. A low 2,3 DPG level shifts the curve to the left with impaired release of oxygen in the tissues. The concentration of 2,3 DPG falls to zero in both ACD and CPD blood after 3 weeks but the *rate* of decay is slower in CPD blood. With a small transfusion of old blood with its low level of 2,3 DPG there may be little clinical effect but if any deficiency exists in the oxygen delivery system for example a low haemotocrit, reduced cardiac output or pulmonary disease then 2,3 DPG depletion may become clinically significant.

Blood is stored at 4–6°C and therefore requires warming prior to transfusion. It contains no ionised Ca although Ca can be readily mobilised from the skeleton to restore plasma levels unless the patient is very poorly perfused. During the period of storage the K content rises and may reach 25 mmol l^{-1} at the end of 3 weeks. Following infusion of stored blood the citrate is metabolised over the next 24 hours to bicarbonate. Hence despite the low pH of stored blood a metabolic alkalosis is a common finding on the following day. The depleted 2,3 DPG levels are restored over the next 24–48 hours. This is very important as any preoperative blood transfusion that may be required should be completed 48 hours before surgery is contemplated.

Blood which is more than 4 days old is unlikely to contain any useful platelets. Indeed after 24 hours the platelet count of stored blood is very much reduced (50–60% of the original level). Platelet concentrates are the best way of dealing with a severe reduction in platelet count and fresh frozen plasma is the best source of clotting factors.

Although stored blood contains no platelets, factor V or factor VIII it does contain very many unwanted particles. These microemboli are made up of platelets and white blood cells which readily pass the standard blood giving set filters and lodge in pulmonary capillaries. Initially (2–7 days) the microemboli consist of platelets. Subsequently degenerate granulocytes and more platelets are added and later on fragmented red blood cells. The number of microaggregates increases with the duration of storage, to 140 000 ml^{-1} or 70 million per unit of blood. Their size ranges from 100–200 μm and they therefore pass through the standard administration set clot screen. Platelets clump more readily in CPD blood which therefore contains more microaggregates during the first week than

ACD blood. After this first week there is no difference between ACD and CPD blood in this respect. The increased acidity of ACD blood seems to prevent platelet aggregation. If 20% or more of a patient's blood volume is replaced with transfused blood then an increase in pulmonary arteriovenous shunting and alveolar to arterial oxygen difference occurs. This can be prevented by filtration through a micropore filter (40 μm) of all blood which is more than 4 days old.

Many febrile transfusion reactions are due to granulocytes; some 11×10^8 leucocytes are necessary for such a reaction to occur. Granulocyte filtration reduces the number of these febrile reactions.

In addition there is a risk of hepatitis when stored blood is given and pyrogenic, haemolytic and allergic reactions may occur (Table 10.3).

Supplies of donated blood are limited in Britain and there is an increasing tendency to process blood to separate it into fractions to be used for specific purposes. If a low haematocrit is present packed red cells should be used. The plasma can then be used for the preparation of cryoprecipitate for factor VIII replacement, fresh frozen plasma or platelet concentrates. If a massive blood transfusion is required then fresh frozen plasma containing clotting factors and platelets will be needed in addition. Rarely Ca may need to be given in situations of very low blood pressure and cardiac output when the skeleton will be adequately perfused to maintain plasma Ca.

The main purpose of transfusing blood is to restore to normal the oxygen carrying capacity of the intravascular volume. There is evidence that blood flow and oxygen delivery are optimal at a haemoglobin concentration of 10 g dl^{-1}.

PLASMA

The preparation of plasma now available is human plasma protein fraction (HPPF). This is an isotonic solution containing in each litre:
    18 g protein.
    140–160 mmol Na.
    < 2 mmol K.
It is a sterile solution and because it is heated to 60°C for 10 hours during preparation it does not carry a risk of hepatitis. This solution is invaluable for replacing the plasma loss from burns and for treating crush injury and pancreatitis. In these situations the

Table 10.3   Hazards of blood transfusion.

---

1   Infection*
   viral hepatitis
   syphilis
   malaria
   cytomegalovirus
   bacterial infection after collection
   Blood should never go back into the refrigerator after 30 minutes at room temperature and packed cells should be used within 6 hours of preparation.
2   Incompatible blood transfusion
   red blood cells
   leucocytes
   platelets
   proteins
3   Air embolus
4   Allergic reactions
5   Non-immunological reactions
   vasoactive substances
   cold blood
   citrate toxicity
   potassium toxicity
   hyperammonaemia: 3 week old stored blood may have an ammonia content of 900 μg dl^{-1}
6   Microaggregates
7   Thrombophlebitis
8   Haemosiderosis

---

* Voluntary donors in this country are screened for syphilis, etc. and blood is taken under strict control. This is not the case in the USA where commercial donors have a higher incidence of undesirable illness.

haematocrit will be raised and serial estimations will be a good guide to the volume of HPPF required. If such plasma losses are replaced with crystalloid a fall in plasma colloid osmotic pressure will occur with increased formation of interstitial water and pulmonary oedema. HPPF is an acid solution with pH 7.0.

DEXTRAN

A typical solution for plasma substitution is 6% dextran 70 which is available in 5% dextrose or 0.9% saline. It has a molecular weight (MW) of about 60 000–70 000 compared to the MW of albumin at 66 000. Dextran 70 is a hypertonic solution. Transfusion of 500 ml results in almost twice this volume of plasma expansion. In normo-volaemic patients the plasma expansion lasts for 4–6 hours but in hypovolaemia expansion lasts longer. 40–70% is excreted in the urine over 24 hours.

Indications for the use of dextran

1 Hypovolaemic shock.
2 Normovolaemic haemodilution in surgical patients.
3 Prevention of thromboembolism associated with surgery.
4 Improving blood flow in a limb with a compromised circulation.

Dextran 40 is the preparation favoured for reducing blood viscosity. Its action is too short to be a useful plasma expander. Dextran 110 is also available. This preparation remains in the circulation longer than the other two.

Contraindications to the use of dextrans are the presence of cardiac failure where volume overload may occur and the presence of a bleeding diathesis in particular a deficiency of platelets. Large quantities of administered dextran interfere with the crossmatching of blood so it is important to take blood for this purpose prior to administering a dextran infusion. Dextran is antigenic and adverse reactions do occur including severe anaphylaxis. In one large series the incidence of shock, cardiac and/or respiratory arrest was found to be:

0.003% for plasma protein solutions.
0.008% for dextran.
0.038% for gelatin solutions.

GELATIN

Haemeccel is a 3.5% solution of degraded gelatin with a MW of 30 000–35 000 and a pH of 7.25. Because of the lower MW it remains in the circulation for a shorter time and its haemodynamic action is limited to about 3 hours. These solutions are quickly excreted by the kidneys, and up to 2500 ml may be given in 24 hours if necessary, whereas excessive doses of dextran especially dextran 40 damage the kidney.

CRYSTALLOID SOLUTIONS

Electrolyte solutions may be indicated for ECF losses but will *not* replace intravascular volume as they are rapidly lost into the interstitial fluid.

If the PCWP is raised in the presence of shock then vasoactive or inotropic drugs for example sodium nitroprusside, nitroglycerine or dopamine may be indicated but further discussion of these is beyond the scope of this book.

Pulmonary oedema will occur if the PCWP is greater than 15–20 mmHg or at a lower value than this if the colloid osmotic pressure is reduced or if the pulmonary capillaries are excessively permeable as in adult respiratory distress syndrome (ARDS).

In these circumstances the gradient (colloid osmotic pressure–PCWP) is valuable since it correlates with the absorptive force tending to keep the alveoli free of oedema fluid.

Endorphines have been implicated recently in the pathophysiology of shock. Naloxone can increase the blood pressure and survival in experimentally induced hypovalaemic shock.

Other preoperative fluid losses should be replaced slowly over 24–48 hours and adequate i.v. therapy given to cover continuing losses.

NORMAL MAINTENANCE REQUIREMENTS

Water   0–10 kg   100 ml kg^{-1} daily
         11–20 kg   1000 ml + 50 ml kg^{-1} daily
         21 kg or more   1500 ml + 25 ml kg^{-1} daily
For an adult this is about 30–35 ml kg^{-1} daily.
Sodium   1–2 mmol kg^{-1} daily
Potassium   1 mmol kg^{-1} daily.

Certain other aspects of preoperative fluid therapy include administration of dextrose and insulin to diabetics and setting up a mannitol infusion in patients with obstructive jaundice to reduce the incidence of acute tubular necrosis.

INTRAOPERATIVE FLUID AND ELECTROLYTE REQUIREMENTS

There are a number of factors to be considered.

The metabolic response to trauma

This has already been described in Chapter 9. It results in the following changes:

1 Urine volume is reduced and its Na content is reduced.
2 Urine K and nitrogen (N_2) content are raised.
3 Plasma Na and albumin are decreased.
4 Plasma ADH, aldosterone, cortisol, catecholamines, insulin, glucose, free fatty acids (FFA) and amino acids (AA) are increased.

Intraoperative factors

Vascular permeability is increased in damaged areas giving rise to increased interstitial fluid. This sequestration into a third space was first described by Shires and his colleagues in the 1960s. It results in a reduced plasma volume. The existence of this third space is disputed; most authorities agreeing with Cleland (1966) that the ECF reduction was overestimated. In some circumstances for example crush injury and bowel obstruction large volumes of fluid are sequestrated but otherwise the importance of the third space is still subject to uncertainty.

Fluid administration

During major surgery a solution such as Hartmann's balanced electrolyte (see below) which resembles ECF is often administered. Urine volume and Na excretion are thereby maintained with less intraoperative hypotension and less postoperative renal failure. However over enthusiastic administration of Hartmann's solution may expand the interstitial fluid especially in the pulmonary circulation leading to pulmonary oedema.

Table 10.4 Composition of intravenous fluids (mmol l^{-1}).

	Na	K	Cl	Ca	Lactate
Hartmann's	131	5	111	2	29
Dextrose + saline (4.3% + 0.18%)	31		31		
0.9% saline	150		150		

Renal impairment

Postoperative renal failure is commoner after cardiopulmonary bypass, aortic or renal vessel surgery and with pre-existing hepatic or renal disease or when hypotension, massive trauma and transfusion have occured. General anaesthetics also may impair renal function.

Fluid replacement

Many operations do not require fluid administration. The volume and composition of fluid required depends upon a number of factors.
1 The pre-existing abnormality which requires correction.
2 The maintenance requirements.
3 The extent of the operation site oedema.
4 The presence of exudates and intestinal secretions.
5 The blood loss.
6 The extent and duration of the operation.

The aim is to give fluid to replace fluid sequestered which is very difficult to measure and to supply basal requirements. Successful treatment also reduces viscous bronchial secretions postoperatively and reduces the sensation of thirst.

Therefore Hartmann's solution may be given to maintain a urine volume of $0.5-1$ ml kg^{-1} hour^{-1}. An alternative is to give 10 ml kg^{-1} for the first hour and 5 ml kg^{-1} during subsequent hours to a maximum volume of 3 litres. Other workers recommend 5 ml kg^{-1} hour^{-1} of surgery to a maximum of $1.5-2$ litres in an adult with a reduction for pre-existing cardiovascular disease. Hartmann's solution is slightly hypotonic in relation to interstitial fluid and therefore will replace the fluid lost during surgery and the insensible water loss due to sweating and respiration. Administration of dextrose saline and 5% dextrose may cause hypotonicity. There is a danger in excessive administration of salt solutions and especial care should be taken *not* to increase the rate of infusion to compensate for a low blood pressure (BP) due to another cause for example anaesthetic drugs. If despite adequate intraoperative fluid administration and in the absence of outstanding loss oliguria persists then 20–40 mg frusemide should be given i.v. Blood loss in excess of 1 litre in an adult requires replacement but losses of less than 1 litre can be replaced with electrolytes. The haemoglobin concentration falls but oxygen carrying capacity is not significantly reduced.

Colloids

These should be reserved for expansion of a reduced intravascular volume when blood is not available. Excessive use of colloid leads to acute circulatory overload because it does not enter interstitial fluid. CVP measurements are valuable during colloid administration.

Special circumstances

Cardiovascular disease

There is a danger of overexpansion of the ECF space. A urinary catheter and CVP may be indicated preoperatively and perhaps inotropic drugs or diuretics. In addition the importance of K replacement in those receiving digoxin and diuretics cannot be overemphasised. A patient should not be presented for surgery with a significant reduction in total body K.

Renal insufficiency

In chronic renal failure fluid depletion may further increase blood urea and creatinine. Dialysis should be manipulated to produce an optimal state for surgery. Methods of protecting the kidney during surgery will be considered in Chapter 11.

Hepatic disease

The dangers include development of renal failure, fluid overload especially if ascites is already present and hypoglycaemia.

If the patient has obstructive jaundice mannitol or frusemide should be administered to prevent renal failure (see Chapter 11).

Prophylaxis of deep vein thrombosis

Dextran given by the following regime has been shown to be as effective as low dose heparin in preventing fatal pulmonary embolus.

Dextran 70 in 0.9% saline, 500 ml:
1   At induction of anaesthesia over 1 hour.
2   Postoperatively over 2 hours.
3   On the first postoperative day over 4 hours.

Recent evidence suggests that blood clots faster when diluted with saline (Janvrin et al 1980). Sixty patients undergoing laparotomy were allocated to two groups only one of which received intraoperative fluid therapy. Those receiving parenteral fluid became hypercoagulable compared to the group not receiving fluid. Postoperative deep vein thrombosis occurred in 30% of the group receiving i.v. fluids (as measured by ^{125}I fibrinogen uptake test) but in only 7% of the group from which fluids were withheld.

POSTOPERATIVE FLUID THERAPY

At this time the patient has the following problems to contend with:
1 The metabolic response to trauma.
2 The third space effects.
3 The effects of anaesthesia and surgery on renal function.
4 The well meaning but puzzled doctor.

Important factors are maintenance of hydration, renal function, blood volume and electrolyte balance. The metabolic response to trauma has been fully considered elsewhere and leads to retention of Na and water. Third space ECF losses continue from the operative into the postoperative period.

Postoperative renal function

After surgery a reduction in urine output is to be expected (Table 10.5). In a stable patient with a given osmolar load for excretion at a fixed GFR and urine flow an increase in distal tubular water reabsorption will reduce urine volume. Another mechanism operating after surgery is the presentation of an increased osmolar load for

Table 10.5 24 hour urine measurements in normal and postoperative states.

	Normal	Post-op	Duration (days)
Volume	1500 ml	500 ml	1–2
Sodium	70 mmol	5–20 mmol	2–5
Potassium	70 mmol	100 mmol	1–3
Nitrogen	8–12 g	10–20 g	4–10

excretion. This may be due to protein catabolism and in the absence of an increased free water excretion this will increase blood urea.

It is important to know what may be considered abnormal. A urine volume of less than 20 ml hourly for 2 or more hours should be considered abnormal because this is less than the minimum urine volume formed with maximum water conservation and minimum solute load. It is however not uncommon for patients to be almost anuric intraoperatively and postoperatively and subsequently to return to normal urine flow. Before embarking upon therapy for oliguria it is essential to check for a blocked urinary catheter.

Unfortunately a urine flow in excess of 20 ml hour^{-1} does not exclude renal dysfunction. Severe intercurrent disease, hypotension and renal disease may present with a urine flow greater than 20 ml hourly in the presence of a rising blood urea. This is probably due to a decreased functioning nephron mass so that total urea excretion is small and urine urea low.

The importance of maintaining renal perfusion intraoperatively and postoperatively cannot be over emphasised. Although the controversial third space losses may in the past have been over-estimated with detrimental pulmonary oedema underestimation is just as dangerous since reduction in ECF and plasma volume will intensify intra and extrarenal mechanisms for Na and water conservation. Although overexpansion of ECF increases Na excretion only a proportion of the extra administered Na load is excreted. (The fraction of the load eliminated remains constant at about 33% under conditions of anaesthesia and surgery.)

Summary of the changes occurring postoperatively

1 Decreased GFR.
2 Increased tubular reabsorption of Na partly due to an increase in aldosterone.
3 Increased collecting duct reabsorption of Na.
4 Increased ADH and water retention.
5 Inability to excrete free water or form hypotonic urine. There is therefore some problem with regard to which fluid to give.
There are two alternatives:
(a) A fluid load may be given to produce a normal urine output, to inhibit ADH response, maintain plasma volume and reduce renal vasoconstriction.

(b) Fluid may be restricted on the grounds that a high fluid regime has little effect on ADH production.

High salt loads are tolerated but not beneficial and a high urine output is only achieved at the expense of positive Na and water balance with ECF expansion. In a healthy person 2 l of 0.9% saline leads to a reduction in pulmonary compliance and continued administration in a postoperative patient may produce pulmonary oedema. In salt load resuscitation of battle casualties pulmonary oedema may have a mortality of up to 80%.

Postoperative requirements

Water requirements

Preoperative requirements and the adequacy of correction of deficits must always be taken into account. Some postoperative water loss may be considered obligatory including insensible loss, urinary loss and dynamic loss.

INSENSIBLE LOSSES

The volume will vary with temperature. There is an increase in insensible loss of 10% per degree centigrade rise in body temperature. This loss also varies with the humidity and factors such as breathing dry anaesthetic gases for a prolonged period. Insensible water gain may also occur due to the production of water of metabolism. This may reach high levels in massive injury, sepsis and fever and is made worse by mobilisation of water from cells into ECF in an amount up to 850 ml daily. Burns lose water by evaporation. In states of water and electrolyte lack decreased insensible loss occurs and there is also wide variations between individuals from day to day.

URINARY LOSSES

The postoperative patient cannot excrete free water or produce a very hypotonic urine for 72 hours after surgery during which time urine osmolality is about 1 mosmol ml^{-1} and 300–400 ml of urine are required to clear the solute load in a starved patient. In catabolism a much larger volume of urine is needed to prevent solute retention. If no intravenous fluid is given to a patient post-operatively then he voluntarily takes about 25 ml kg^{-1} of water daily. Therefore administration of free water should perhaps be limited to this volume in the absence of increased water loss. Administration of 5% dextrose constitutes a water load which given in excess may lead to water intoxication over 48–72 hours.

DYNAMIC LOSSES

Normal gastrointestinal secretions are reabsorbed but fluid loss due to vomiting and from fistulae should be taken into account. Ileal, biliary, and pancreatic fluid losses have an electrolyte content similar to 0.9% saline with 5 mmol K in each litre (see Table 10.1). Colonic losses and those above the pylorus are best replaced with 0.45% saline with 5 mmol K in each litre. Protein loss may also require replacement. Fistulae losses however are usually of mixed origin and therefore should have their electrolyte content measured.

Electrolyte requirements

SODIUM

An excessive Na load requires 2–3 days for excretion. Normal Na requirements are 80–100 mmol (1–2 mmol kg^{-1}) daily but postoperatively there is virtually no Na requirement in the absence of excessive loss. Children normally require about 2 mmol kg^{-1} Na daily. Certainly in patients with pulmonary, renal or cardiac disease salt restriction is indicated unless chronic renal failure with fixed Na and water loss is present when rapid hypovolaemia may occur with such restrictions.

POTASSIUM

Losses are 70–90 mmol daily (1–1.5 mmol kg^{-1}). Since immediate postoperative renal function is uncertain K should not be given on the first postoperative day. Thereafter 50 mmol should be given daily and this should be increased depending on losses and plasma levels. If K is not given postoperatively the tendency for Na to be retained is prolonged and intensified. Aldosterone increases post-operative urinary K loss.

MAGNESIUM

5 mmol are lost in the urine daily. Replacement is only important with long term parenteral therapy.

CALCIUM

The vast stores in the skeleton replace plasma Ca in the immediate postoperative period.

Blood, albumin and other colloids should be used as required and are discussed elsewhere.

If fluid replacement is judged to be adequate and urine output is poor it is important when diuretic therapy is contemplated to consider the state of the cardiovascular system. Administration of frusemide results in a reduction in cardiac output, an increase in peripheral vascular resistance and in a fall in systemic and pulmonary arterial pressures. Mannitol on the other hand causes an increase in cardiac output and pulmonary arterial pressure. Peripheral resistance is decreased. Therefore for postoperative oliguria in the absence of known cardiovascular disease mannitol is the diuretic of choice.

Planning of postoperative fluid regime

The nature of the surgery and the current fluid balance of the patient are of paramount importance here. It is known that 3 litres of water daily puts most patients into marked positive water balance but 1.5 litres of 5% dextrose with no added salt very rarely produces hyponatraemia in the absence of large abnormal salt losses. One litre of 0.9% saline daily leads to weight gain and Na retention. In the postoperative period hyponatraemia is almost always due to administration of excessive water as 5% dextrose.

A slightly dry but stable patient is the aim. Currently overhydration is more of a problem in surgical patients than underhydration especially in the elderly, after trauma and intracranial surgery. Elective surgery of moderate severity can be accomplished without i.v. fluids and the patients come to no harm.

The following recommendations can be made:

1 Give blood to keep the haemoglobin greater than 10 g dl^{-1}.

2 Maintain a urine output in excess of 400 ml daily. A greater urine output should be aimed for if there is an increased solute load for excretion.

3 1.5 litres of 5% dextrose over 24 hours will replace insensible loss, reduce N$_2$ loss and maintain urine output.

4 No Na need be given for 3 days if there is no loss. This situation is rare so that a compromise is to give dextrose 4.3% saline 0.18% if minimal ECF losses are occurring. This contains Na 31 mmol l^{-1}. Hartmann's solution is more appropriate if ECF losses are raised.

5 Afer the first day 1 mmol kg^{-1} of K should be given daily as KCl.

6 Plasma albumin should be maintained in excess of 35 g l^{-1}.

7 Abnormal gastrointestinal losses should be replaced.

Mg, vitamins and zinc are required during prolonged i.v. therapy and parenteral nutrition should be considered as suggested in Chapter 12.

Intravenous therapy should be continued until oral fluids can be taken in adequate volume. Great care should be taken not to overload the patient at this time. As oral intake is increased a reduction in i.v. fluids is appropriate.

Examples

1 Cholecystectomy.
Intraoperatively. 1 litre Hartmann's solution for ECF replacement.
Postoperatively. 1.5 litres 5% dextrose and 0.5 litres Hartmann's solution for ECF replacement over 24 hours.

2 Major surgery involving prolonged exposure of a body cavity for example thoracoabdominal oesophagogastrectomy or aortic aneurysm repair.
Intraoperatively. (a) 1–3 litres Hartmann's solution for ECF replacement. The volume will depend on CVP and haematocrit values.
(b) 250 ml hour^{-1} 5% dextrose will cover evaporative losses due to visceral exposure.
Postoperatively. 1.5–2 litres 5% dextrose and 0.5–1 litres Hartmann's solution for ECF replacement over 24 hours.

Chapter 11
Problems of Renal Disease

As renal disease produces progressive loss of renal substance or an acute event precipitates renal failure profound effects on fluid and electrolyte balance are to be expected. Today sophisticated management in specialist centres can significantly reduce mortality and morbidity in renal disease.

Fig. 11.1 shows the expected plasma and urine consitituents in health. Wide variations occur in urine constituents during illness.

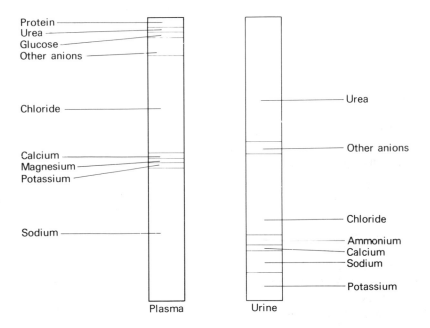

Fig. 11.1 Constituents of plasma and urine. It must be remembered that wide variations will occur in urine constituents during illness.

ACUTE RENAL FAILURE

This is still a devastating illness occurring uncommonly (1–2 per thousand acute hospital admissions), which is often diagnosed by the sudden onset of oliguria. The definition of oliguria in these circumstances is less than 400 ml of urine over 24 hours in an adult. Early diagnosis and referral are essential since the mortality of acute renal failure (ARF) in a nonspecialist unit is 90%.

Clinical accompaniments of ARF

1   Blood urea, creatinine and uric acid are raised.
2   H, K, Mg, PO_4 and sulphate levels in plasma are increased.
3   Impaired salt and water excretion leads in severe cases to oedema. Water retention is usually in excess of salt retention.
4   Plasma HCO_3 falls because HCO_3 buffers the acidic ions which the kidney is unable to excrete. Hyperventilation usually occurs but fails to completely prevent the fall in pH.
   Most patients will be oliguric but the same clinical picture may occur in the presence of polyuric renal failure, when a large urine volume of low osmolality is produced.

Causes of acute renal failure

These classically can be usefully divided into prerenal, renal and postrenal causes.

Prerenal causes

1   Hypovolaemia:
   haemorrhage
   burns
   other large plasma losses
   dehydration.
2   Cardiogenic shock:
   postmyocardial infarction
   massive pulmonary embolus
   aortic dissection
   following cardiopulmonary bypass.
3   Septicaemia
4   Liver disease:

cirrhosis
jaundice.
5 Acute haemolysis:
incompatible blood transfusion
falciparum malaria.
6 Obstetric disasters:
eclampsia
septic abortion
postpartum haemorrhage.
7 Acute pancreatitis:

Malignant hypertension, hypercalcaemia, drug overdose, hyperuricaemia and renal transplantation may also be aetiological factors. A prerenal cause for renal failure may be obvious. The two most important aetiological factors are acute circulatory failure and a disturbance of electrolyte balance. Recognition of situations in which ARF is likely have lead to improved prophylaxis.

If the patient's condition permits, blood pressure measurements in the supine and upright positions may demonstrate a postural fall in blood pressure indicating a reduced blood volume. Initially simple measures such as urine specific gravity, microscopy and examination of a spun urine specimen may be helpful.

Early appraisal of plasma volume, cardiac function, central venous pressure monitoring, an indwelling arterial cannula for pressure monitoring and Swan Ganz catheter for pulmonary capillary wedge pressure monitoring may provide information for therapy to prevent ARF. It is important also to recognise that severe infection in the surgical patient is very likely to be associated with ARF.

If a patient is known to be at high risk during surgery for example those with obstructive jaundice prophylactic treatment in this case with mannitol may avert renal failure. Patients for lower bowel surgery should receive prophylactic antibiotics. In the absence of preexisting renal disease patients with prerenal ARF usually have a disproportionate rise in blood urea compared to creatinine, and a plasma creatinine greater than 250 μmol l^{-1} is associated with a 90% chance of preexisting renal impairment.

RENAL RESPONSE TO A POOR PERFUSION STATE

Small volumes of urine will be excreted with the following characteristics:

1 A high osmolality, certainly greater than 600 mosmol kg⁻¹ and a urine:plasma osmolality ratio of 1.3–2.0

2 A low Na concentration (less than 10 mmol l⁻¹).

3 A high urine to plasma urea and creatinine ratio (greater than 10 to 1).

If the underlying aetiological factors in the development of pre-renal ARF are not corrected than established ARF occurs and then restoration of the circulating blood volume will not improve the situation although it is still essential.

RENAL RESPONSE IN ESTABLISHED ACUTE RENAL FAILURE

Small volumes of urine are excreted with the following characteristics:

1 A urine osmolality which is almost isotonic with plasma (approximately 300 mosmol kg⁻¹) and a urine:plasma osmolality ratio of less than 1.2:1.

2 A high concentration of Na. Urine Na will be greater than 20 mmol l⁻¹ or more if diuretics are used.

3 A low urine:plasma urea and creatinine ratio (less than 10:1). Plasma urea and creatinine rise progressively.

In the differential diagnosis of ARF in patients with a raised plasma urea or creatinine it has been shown by some authors that tests based on urine constituents are imprecise. In these circumstances the fractional excretion of Na is more valuable. This is calculated as follows from the plasma and urine Na and creatinine.

$$\frac{\text{urine Na}}{\text{plasma Na}} \div \frac{\text{urine creatinine}}{\text{plasma creatinine}} \times 100$$

If this value is greater than 1 then ARF is due to:

1 Acute tubular necrosis-oliguric or nonoliguric, or

2 Urinary tract obstruction.

If this value is less than 1 then the cause is:

1 Prerenal ARF, or

2 Acute glomerulonephritis.

This test should not be used in patients with chronic renal disease, interstitial nephropathy, glycosuria or in those receiving diuretics.

Renal causes of ARF

1 Rapidly progressive glomerulonephritis:
post streptococcal glomerulonephritis
goodpasture's syndrome
polyarteritis nodosa
systemic lupus erythematosis.
2 Acute interstitial nephritis. This may be caused by methicillin or other antibiotics, phenytoin and many other drugs.
3 Haemolytic uraemic syndrome.
4 Nephrotoxic agents:
heavy metals
lead
gold
inorganic compounds
aniline dyes
organic compounds
paraquat
carbon tetrachloride
radiographic contrast media.
Renal biopsy confirms the diagnosis and management is essentially that of the underlying condition, stopping all nephrotoxic agents and treating the associated hypertension.

Acute decompensation of renal function may occur in patients with pre-existing chronic renal failure.

Postrenal causes of ARF

1 Renal calculi.
2 Analgesic nephropathy producing papillary obstruction.
3 Retroperitoneal fibrosis.
4 Stricture.
5 Carcinomas:
bladder
cervix
prostate
rectum.
6 Dysproteinaemias: multiple myeloma.
7 Crystalluria. sulphonamides.
8 Hyperuricaemia.

Management includes confirmation of the diagnosis by high dose excretion urography, surgical investigation and treatment of the underlying cause.

In ARF renal blood flow is reduced (40% of normal) but GFR is almost zero. Renal renin levels are raised and locally produced angiotensin II in the renal cortex may be the cause of afferent arteriolar vasoconstriction. Intravascular coagulation is known to be important in the production of many cases of established renal failure.

Following ARF due to prerenal causes an oliguric phase lasts 1–3 weeks with a variable increase in plasma urea and creatinine, an increasing acidosis and hyperkalaemia. Urine output subsequently rises during recovery and the diuretic phase begins.

Mannitol test

A response to mannitol distinguishes a hypovolaemic situation from established ARF. 100 ml of 20% mannitol are infused over 10 minutes. Urine output should increase by 50% over the next 2 hours. If this is not the case then the test can be repeated to a maximum of 100 g mannitol over 24 hours. If the blood volume is known to be high then this test may precipitate heart failure and doses of frusemide up to 1 g should be used instead. The response to a small conventional dose should be tried first. It must be remembered that the combination of certain antibiotics such as gentamicin with frusemide may precipitate ARF.

Dopamine

Some workers have used a low dose dopamine infusion in incipient acute tubular necrosis to prevent oliguria. $0.5-3$ μg kg^{-1} min^{-1} dopamine stimulates renal dopamine receptors producing vaso-dilatation of the afferent arterioles and a diuresis. The action of frusemide may be synergistic because the dopamine induced vaso-dilatation allows frusemide access to the loops of Henle whence it increases salt and water excretion. Increased urine flow at the macula densa may inhibit the renin-angiotensin system and hence antagonise the vasoconstriction in afferent arterioles induced by angiotensin II.

Frusemide combined with dopamine prevents the inhibition of

prostaglandin migration to the macula densa which may be an important factor in early renal failure (see Chapter 2).

In established ARF administration of excess dopamine concentrations may have a deleterious effect by redistributing renal blood flow. This is directly analagous to the alpha vasoconstrictor effects of dopamine on the peripheral circulation. Therefore a small dose of dopamine may be used for its direct renal effects. Less than 10 μg kg^{-1} min^{-1} will produce a positive inotropic effect on the myocardium which may improve GFR and urine flow. Doses greater than this are *contraindicated* since peripheral vasoconstriction will occur and renal cortical necrosis may be precipitated.

Management of acute renal failure

1 Identify *all* underlying causes. Chronic renal failure may coexist with acute hypovolaemia in large bowel obstruction. Always suspect and look for septicaemia.
2 Fluids. Fluid management follows the lines suggested in Chapter 10 on preoperative fluid resuscitation. The CVP should be kept at 6–8 cm water.
3 Appropriate treatment should be given for cardiogenic shock and may include the use of inotropic agents or sodium nitroprusside.

If oliguria persists after resuscitation the use of diuretics should be considered (see above). The rapid injection of frusemide in high doses may be associated with ventricular arrythmias. Bumetanide may be a better loop diuretic in these circumstances. If oliguria persists despite two large doses of diuretic then ARF is established.

Management of fully established
acute renal failure

Assessment of fluid balance

Accurate fluid balance monitoring is essential since overhydration readily produces pulmonary oedema. All fluid lost should be measured and its electrolyte content ascertained in the laboratory. Losses should be replaced.

Daily weighing is invaluable. Weighing beds are available on many renal units. Weight gain is almost always due to fluid retention.

Fluid administration

Fluid should be given to replace:
1   Insensible loss. In an adult this is about 500 ml daily.
2   The previous day's urine output.
3   The previous day's other losses.
Febrile or burned patients will have increased requirements.

Electrolyte administration

SODIUM

Urinary and other measured Na losses should be replaced unless
heart failure or oedema dictate Na restriction.

POTASSIUM

Plasma K is likely to be raised. In addition to the renal failure sepsis
and hypercatabolism will increase plasma K by release of intracellular K. If plasma K exceeds 6 mmol l^{-1} urgent measures are
required to reduce it and prevent cardiac arrest in asystole.

Methods of reducing plasma potassium acutely
1   Soluble insulin 10–20 units should be given intravenously with
25–50 g glucose. This manoeuvre promotes uptake of K into cells
with glucose facilitated by insulin.
2   Calcium chloride or gluconate 5–10 mmol given intravenously
will protect the heart against the adverse effects of a raised K. This
should only be given with continuous ECG monitoring. The dose
may need repeating.
3   Sodium bicarbonate should be given intravenously. This will
correct the metabolic acidosis and tend to reduce plasma K. Unfortunately this involves giving a salt load.

Exchange resins
An exchange resin in the calcium form such as calcium resonium 15
g should be given 8 hourly. This is a relatively slow form of treatment. A persistently raised plasma K is an indication that dialysis
will be necessary.

A positive nitrogen (N_2) balance will prevent catabolism and it is
illogical to starve a patient in ARF. Adequate calories and N_2 must

be given to prevent hypercatabolism and cover energy needs whilst dialysis is undertaken to prevent fluid overload and to reduce plasma K, urea and creatinine. 25–30% of lean body mass may be lost during the course of ARF and subsequent weakness will prolong recovery.

Antibiotics may be required for specific infection with modification of the dose for nephrotoxic drugs. Diuretics may also be indicated.

Patients with ARF should be transferred *early* to a specialist unit for further diagnostic procedures and dialysis. A plot of the weight corrected plasma creatinine against time may allow prediction of the time for dialysis. A plasma urea greater than 30 mmol l^{-1} is unlikely to respond to conservative measures.

CHRONIC RENAL FAILURE

Causes of chronic renal failure

1 Glomerulonephritis.
2 Pyelonephritis.
3 Polycystic kidney.
4 Diabetic nephropathy.
5 Hypertensive renal disease.
6 Analgesic nephropathy.
7 Hereditary and other.

As renal function progressively fails there is an increase in blood urea, creatinine and uric acid. When 70–80% of the nephrons are destroyed the kidney is unable to regulate water, salt and acid base balance. One of two things may happen:
(a) Dehydration with reduction in circulating blood volume may occur.
(b) Oedema or overhydration may occur.
If significant tubular damage occurs then the ability to reabsorb water or electrolyte selectively or to produce HCO_3 is impaired and there is a failure to respond to aldosterone and ADH. Plasma HCO_3 falls and the hydrogen ion concentration rises as does that of sulphate, phoshate and other inorganic anions. Anaemia occurs due to marrow suppression because of reduced erthropoietin levels, toxic factors, reduced intake of haematinics, occult blood loss into the gut and defective platelets leading to coagulation problems.

Endocrine disturbance may affect electrolyte balance and secondary hyperparathyroidism and osteomalacia occur.

In a few patients there is an early increase in plasma renin levels and angiotensin induced hypertension occurs. Aldosterone levels may be raised although less often hypoaldosteronism occurs.

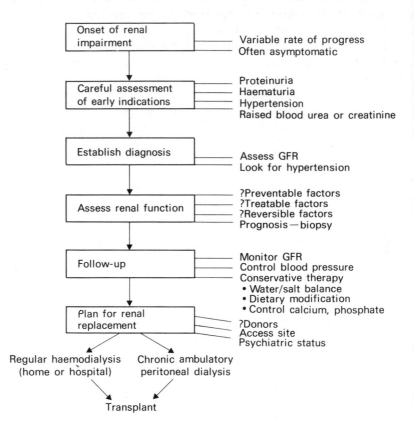

Fig. 11.2 Assessment and management of chronic renal failure.

Creatinine clearance measurements or serial plasma creatinine may be used to assess progress of the disease. Clearance is a concept calculated from the concentration of a substance in the urine multiplied by the urine flow per unit of time and divided by the plasma concentration of the substance.

Creatinine clearance =

$$\frac{\text{urine creatinine} \times \text{urine flow per unit time}}{\text{plasma creatinine}}$$

This is usually related to surface area (calculated from weight and height) and the normal range is 40–75 ml min^{-1} m^{-2}.

Very important aspects of management include:

1 Treatment of uncontrolled hypertension.
2 Treatment of urinary tract infection or obstruction.
3 Avoidance of dehydration.
4 Avoidance of nephrotoxic drugs.

In those cases in which water and Na retention occur diuretics may reduce oedema and controlled water and salt intake may reduce plasma creatinine. Plasma K may even fall on dietary restriction if there is impaired tubular reabsorption. Early control of Ca and PO$_4$ level is important and may delay renal osteodystrophy. A small increase in plasma PO$_4$ due to reduction in GFR may transiently reduce plasma Ca and stimulate parathormone production.

Methods of reducing plasma phosphate

1 Drugs which bind phosphate in the gut such as aluminium hydroxide will reduce absorption of phosphate but unfortunately aluminium increases the incidence of dialysis dementia.
2 Reduction in dietary phosphate is very difficult but calcium supplements can be given.
3 If bone disease is progressive vitamin D analogues may be indicated (see Chapter 8). Dietary protein restriction is indicated if patients cannot be accepted for dialysis or transplantation.

Nephrotic syndrome

There is increased permeability of the glomerular basement membrane with leakage of plasma proteins into the urine. As a result plasma protein concentration falls, there is a reduction in circulating blood volume, activation of the renin angiotensin systme and aldosterone release. Sodium retention then occurs. ADH secretion is increased and oedema occurs. The secondary hyperaldosteronism also produces bicarbonate retention, alkalosis and a fall in plasma

K. Renal biopsy aids management. If a minimal change appearance is seen these cases respond well to steroid therapy.

Difficulties in the diagnosis of renal failure

1   After surgery urinary output is expected to be less than normal so that oliguria as a criterion of renal failure may be misleading at this time (see Chapter 10).

2   Blood urea may rise after surgery due to increased tissue breakdown with fixed free water excretion. Increased water reabsorption will similarly reduce urine output.

3   In an adult a urine flow less than 20 ml hour^{-1} for two consecutive hours is abnormal because it is less than the minimum urine volume found with maximum water conservation and minimum solute load.

Prevention of renal failure at this time hinges on avoiding circulatory insufficiency and maintenance of urine output despite endocrine influences.

Methods of renal protection in the perioperative period

1   Prime the patient with Hartmann's solution to increase ECF by 1 litre. Certain patients are at increased risk of developing renal failure. These include those undergoing cardiopulmonary bypass, aortic clamping, those with obstructive jaundice or suffering severe blood loss. Any technique which reduces sodium reabsorption should be beneficial. This includes administration of mannitol, frusemide or ethacrynic acid or even sodium itself.

2   Mannitol in a dose of 15 g (0.25 g kg^{-1}) may be given over 10 minutes 2 hourly for the duration of the risk to a maximum of 100 g daily. This form of protection is also of value when radiographic contrast media are used in the presence of renal disease. Mannitol however causes an increase in cardiac output and pulmonary artery pressure. There is a risk of precipitating heart failure especially in the elderly.

3   Frusemide in a dose of 40 mg 2 hourly. Urine loss should be replaced with 0.45% saline in dextrose with added K if a fall in plasma K occurs. Frusemide and ethacrynic acid increase renal blood flow and GFR during anaesthesia and surgery.

In the situation of extreme fluid loss the oliguria does not always respond to fluid replacement alone but will respond to frusemide or mannitol in addition. If oliguria still persists acute renal failure is established and although this may respond to massive doses of frusemide more usually blood urea and potassium continue to rise.

Dialysis

Removal of substances normally excreted by the kidney by dialysis across a semipermeable membrane is now commonplace.

Peritoneal dialysis (PD)

This simple technique can be undertaken in any hospital ward and may be used for some patients with acute renal failure. It has been used successfully in the management of severe congestive cardiac failure, acute pancreatitis and some cases of poisoning. Recent abdominal surgery precludes this method of dialysis as do extensive burns of the anterior abdominal wall.

The complication rate of this technique is now acceptably low but meticulous attention to detail is essential to reduce infection. A cannula is introduced into the peritoneal cavity avoiding perforation of the viscera, and using a sterile technique. Two litres of dialysis fluid at 37°C is run into the peritoneal cavity through the cannula and out again into a drainage system. The time and volume of this fluid should be recorded as it is run into the peritoneal cavity and on its return to the drainage system. Accurate weighing of the patient is invaluable during this procedure.

COMPLICATIONS

1 Bowel perforation.
2 Perforation of a blood vessel.
3 Perforation of the bladder.
4 Infection. This is the most important problem. Abdominal wall sepsis may occur or peritonitis due to bacteria or fungi.
5 Failure to drain off dialysis fluid. This is commoner in the obese and may be due to loculation or fibrin obstruction in the catheter. It also occurs if the catheter is misplaced or with an excessively long

dwell time. If 2 litres of positive balance occurs PD should be discontinued pending further investigation.

6 Protein loss.

7 Basal pulmonary collapse. This occurs when large volumes of PD fluid splint the diaphragm, reducing movement of the basal lung segments predisposing to collapse.

8 Hypernatraemia.

9 Hyperglycaemia.

10 If fluid is withdrawn from the patient excessively rapidly hypotension and shock may occur.

There are two commercially available PD fluids:

(a) 1.36 g dl^{-1} glucose and osmolality 370 mosmol kg^{-1}. This should remove 1–2 litres of water per day.

(b) 6.36 g dl^{-1} glucose, osmolality 670 mosmol kg^{-1}. This removes more water but is likely to require more insulin for control of blood sugar, to prevent hyperglycaemia.

Heparin is sometimes added to PD fluid to help maintain catheter patency. This practice may make traumatic bleeding worse.

The aim in treating ARF is to keep blood urea less than 35 mmol l^{-1} and plasma creatinine less than 1000 μmol^{-1}.

Chronic peritoneal dialysis

This should only be managed in special units. The patient is likely to require about 40 hours each week of peritoneal dialysis. In fact some of the complications of renal failure may improve more readily with PD than with haemodialysis.

Peritoneal dialysis is unsuitable for the management of the hypercatabolic patient as it cannot reduce the blood urea sufficiently. However it can:

1 Correct acidosis.

2 Return electrolytes to normal.

3 Remove fluid.

Dialysis fluid should always replace essential ions. Mg, Ca, Na and K must be added according to the patient's requirements.

Continuous amubulatory peritoneal dialysis (CAPD)

This is a new technique involving the continuous presence of dialysis fluid in the peritoneal cavity except for periods of 20–40 minutes when the patient changes the fluid for a fresh solution. A soft permanent indwelling catheter is inserted through the abdominal wall into the peritoneal cavity. This is connected via a transfer set to a flexible plastic bag containing the dialysing solution (Fig. 11.3). The bag is raised to shoulder level and emptied into the peritoneal cavity by gravity. The bag is rolled up and retained under the patient's clothing during the dwell time and then lowered to below the peritoneal cavity to drain the solution out.

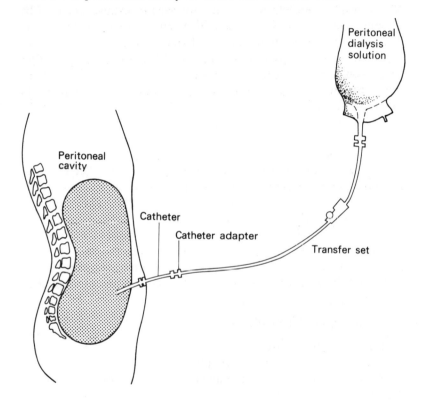

Peritoneal dialysis solution

Peritoneal cavity

Catheter

Catheter adapter

Transfer set

Fig. 11.3 Closed system for continuous ambulatory peritoneal dialysis.

Four to eight hours dwell time is allowed between exchanges. There is a high degree of removal of urea, creatinine and higher molecular weight solutes.

The advantages of the technique are:

1 Better plasma biochemistry with a higher haemoglobin and lower plasma phosphate than with haemodialysis.

2 The cost is about half that of home haemodialysis.

3 Patient independence and rehabilitation. The technique allows a near normal diet, everyday mobility and also allows the renal failure patient to take a holiday.

The main disadvantage is sepsis. Recurrent peritonitis is a problem for which prophylactic cephelexin has proved ineffective. The patient needs a training period. With a meticulous sterile technique and continuing improvement in catheter designs and connections the incidence of sepsis may be reduced. CAPD needs further assessment especially of long term problems meanwhile it offers interesting possibilities for the management of chronic renal failure in specialist units.

Haemodialysis

The great advantage of this technique over PD is its much greater efficiency. Urea clearance is almost four times greater than with PD (150 ml min^{-1} compared to 40 ml min^{-1} for PD). This therefore reduces dialysis time in the chronic situation.

Haemodialysis (HD) allows much greater patient mobility, is much more comfortable for the patient and does not cause protein depletion or basal lung collapse. Although it is more efficient it may be less safe by removing too much fluid from the patient too quickly.

Disadvantages of haemodialysis

1 Special units required.

2 Vascular access may be difficult.

3 Hypotensive patients may have inadequate blood flow through the dialyser.

4 Heparin may be a hazard.

5 Dialysis dementia. The prevalence of this has recently been put at 600 per 100 000 European dialysis patients. Dementia appears to be due to aluminium toxicity.

6 Emotional problems. Dialysis obviously disrupts family life and employment.

Vascular access is via:

(a) Arteriovenous fistula.

(b) Arteriovenous shunt.

(c) As a temporary measure percutaneous cannulation of the femoral vein for access to the inferior vena cava.

WHEN TO DIALYSE

Ideally in ARF blood urea should be kept below 35 mmol l^{-1}. Therefore dialysis should be started early, and repeated regularly and frequently. This is of tremendous value in hypercatabolic patients since it permits adequate parenteral nutrition to be administered. In chronic renal failure a creatinine clearance of less than 10 ml min^{-1} should be treated by dialysis. Other indications for dialysis include a very high plasma potassium (greater than 6 mmol l^{-1}) and severe positive fluid balance.

In the best run dialysis units biochemical parameters are not entirely normal. Plasma creatinine is always raised. Severe oliguria usually occurs when haemodialysis is started and fluid restriction may be necessary. Anaemia and renal osteodystrophy may still be problems and there is no doubt that family life is disrupted.

Renal transplantation provides an alternative to chronic haemodialysis or continuous ambulatory peritoneal dialysis but is beyond the scope of this book.

In acute renal failure dialysis should be continued into the diuretic phase since although urine flow increases GFR may recover more slowly. Indications to stop dialysis include an improvement in blood and urine biochemistry.

Daily urea and electrolyte measurements are of course mandatory.

Chapter 12
Parenteral Nutrition

There is nothing new under the sun, only that which is rediscovered. Parenteral nutrition is not a new field. In 1658 Sir Christopher Wren, scientist and architect, predicted that it should be possible to inject any liquid into the blood stream. In 1664 intravenous wine was used, in 1859 intravenous milk was given for cholera and in 1895 camphor oil was tried intravenously in cardiac patients as a calorie source. Recent surveys show that up to 50% of hospital patients suffer some form of malnutrition during their hospital stay (clinical or biochemical). More than 30% loss of body weight in acute illness is usually fatal. If rapid weight loss occurs in hyper-catabolism then a 15% weight loss may be fatal. Each gram of nitrogen lost is equivalent to a loss of 6.25 g of protein which is equivalent to 30 g muscle mass.

There is no doubt that parenteral nutrition is inferior to enteral nutrition and is associated with a high risk of complications. Total parenteral nutrition (TPN) involves the infusion into a central vein of adequate nutritional requirements.

Various factors contribute to malnutrition in hospital patients. Pre-existing gastrointestinal pathology impairing absorption, fear of eating and therapeutical withdrawal of food are but a few. The metabolic response to trauma has already been described (see Chapter 9).

STARVATION

1 During short-term starvation (a few days) the body requires a minimum of about 180 g glucose for central nervous system and red blood cell metabolism. Initially this glucose is derived from mobil-isation of liver glycogen but reserves of this are very small (Table 12.1) so that glucose is derived from gluconeogenesis. The main substrates for this gluconeogenesis are lactate, pyruvate, alanine, glucogenic amino acids and glycerol. This creates an overall loss of protein. In addition there is increased lipolysis in adipose tissue,

with release of free fatty acids (FFAs). These FFAs are either used directly as fuel and oxidised or are converted by the liver into ketone bodies.

Table 12.1 Energy stores of a 70 kg man.

	kg	Duration	kcal
Carbohydrate (mainly liver glycogen)	0.2	6–12 hours	800
Fat	12–15	20–25 days	109 000–136 000
Protein (mainly muscle)	4–6	10–12 days	16 000– 24 000

2 If starvation is prolonged, ketone adaptation occurs.
(a) The brain begins to utilise ketone bodies as an energy source, thereby reducing glucose requirements by 50% and reducing gluconeogenesis.
(b) Hepatic glucose production falls dramatically.
(c) Urine urea falls, as there is less breakdown of body protein for gluconeogenesis.
(d) Blood ketone body levels rise from a normal fasting value of 0.05–0.50 mmol^{-1} to 4–6 mmol^{-1}. This may be associated with mild metabolic acidosis.
(e) The increase in FFA and ketone bodies inhibits glucose oxidation in muscle and peripheral tissues.
(f) Basal metabolic rate falls with a resultant fall in total calorie requirement.
(g) Tri-iodothyronine (T3) concentration falls and this reduces nitrogen breakdown.

Insulin

This is the main anabolic hormone. Its secretion is stimulated by carbohydrate and protein feeding. Under the influence of insulin body stores of glycogen, protein and fat are built up. Glucose uptake into tissues is promoted, where it provides a source of energy. Lipolysis is then inhibited.

Growth hormone

This is also an anabolic hormone. Uptake of amino acids into cells is promoted for protein synthesis.

Under conditions of stress ketoadaptation breaks down and glucagon, cortisol, and catecholamines oppose the action of insulin with resulting catabolism. Gluconeogenesis, lipolysis and protein breakdown all occur. Whether the body is in a state of anabolism or catabolism depends upon the relative amounts of these hormones present at the time. In conditions of simple starvation, the concentration of insulin slowly decreases and a relative excess of catabolic hormones exists. However, this situation is well regulated, quite unlike the situation in stress when large amounts of catabolic hormones cause considerable breakdown of body tissues. The extent of the metabolic response in surgical patients varies with the nature of the operation, but even uncomplicated, superficial, surgical procedures will increase the metabolic rate by about 10%. This problem is more fully discussed in Chapters 9 and 10.

ASSESSMENT OF NUTRITION

Table 12.1 lists those factors which constitute evidence of nutritional depletion. It has been shown recently that age, weight, weight loss and plasma albumin are not significantly related to post-operative complications, but arm muscle circumference, grip-testing and immunocompetence are useful predictors of morbidity. In any assessment of the nutritional status, it is important to take the overall clinical picure into account. For example, it may be extremely difficult to weigh a critically ill patient at all and a plasma albumin estimation during an albumin infusion is valueless.

Albumin levels are not useful as an early indicator of malnutrition because the levels change slowly in response to a change in nutrition, but the following may be taken as a guide-line:

Plasma albumin $28-35 \text{ g l}^{-1}$ = mild visceral protein depletion.

Plasma albumin $21-27 \text{ g l}^{-1}$ = moderate visceral protein depletion.

Plasma albumin   less than 21 g l^{-1} = severe visceral protein depletion.

Triceps skin fold thickness (TST) is related to fat reserves and can

Table 12.2 Evidence of nutritional depletion.

Recent weight loss > 10%
Serum albumin < 35 g l^{-1}
Serum transferrin < 2 g l^{-1}
Triceps skin fold thickness
   < 10 mm in males
   < 13 mm in females
Mid-arm circumference
   < 23 cm in males
   < 22 cm in females
Lymphopenia < 1.2 × 10^9 l^{-1}
Skin anergy to a battery of antigens
   Candida
   mumps
   streptokinase
   streptodornase
   dermatophytin
   PPD
Dynamometry
3-Methylhistidine
Calculation of mid-arm muscle circumference
   (arm circumference — π × triceps skin thickness)
Creatinine excretion index

---

be measured with Holtain skin fold calipers. A value of less than 80% predicted indicates malnutrition. Mid-arm circumference is useful to calculate the mid-arm muscle circumference (MAMC) which is related to protein stores.

$$\text{MAMC} = \text{mid-arm curcumference} - \pi \text{ (TST)}$$

Mid-arm circumference should be measured with the arm flexed.

Immunocompetence

A battery of antigens can be applied to the skin to test for delayed hypersensitivity. A negative response to these antigens indicates skin anergy and impaired cell mediated immunity.

3-methylhistidine is a non-recyclable muscle metabolite. Increased urinary excretion of 3-methylhistidine implies increased muscle turnover. Retinol binding protein and thyroxine binding prealbumin are both proteins with a more rapid turnover than plasma albumin (half life 14 days) and therefore shows a more rapid improvement in response to treatment for malnutrition, and can be used to assess effectiveness of therapy.

Hand-grip dynamometry is a simple, useful predictor of post-operative complications due to malnutrition. A reduction in grip strength to less than 85% predicted is significant.

Creatinine excretion index

This compares the patient's 24 hour creatinine excretion with the situation in the normal population and is calculated as follows:

$$\frac{\text{Actual 24 hour creatinine excretion} \times 100}{\text{Predicted creatinine excretion}}$$

Tables are available for prediction of the normal creatinine excretion related to size.

Values of 60–80% of normal = mild somatic protein depletion.
Values of 40–50% of normal = moderate somatic protein depletion.
Values of less than 40% of normal = severe somatic protein depletion.

Results of malnutrition

1 Poor tissue healing.
2 Wound breakdown.
3 Anastomotic breakdown.
4 Infection occurs readily and the defence response to it is impaired.
5 Muscle weakness which is particularly important in the respiratory muscles.

The gastrointestinal tract is the preferred route for replacement of any nutritional deficiency. TPN is costly (£200 or more each week) and associated with many more complications than feeding by the enteral route.

If a decision is made to embark upon total parenteral nutrition preoperatively, for example in a patient with carcinoma of oesophagus, where the weight loss may be extreme (up to 30 kg) then at least 2 weeks TPN is required to have any effect on nutri-

Table 12.3 Indications for total parenteral nutrition.

Pre-operative
  carcinoma oesophagus
  pyloric stenosis
Chronic gastrointestinal disease
  Crohn's
  short bowel syndrome
Acute hypercatabolism
  multiple trauma
  burns
  septicaemia
Postoperative
  major GI surgery
  fistulae
Cachexia

---

tional parameters. To embark upon a shorter period to 'top up' the patient will do little except reverse the patient's ketoadaptation to starvation and impair the efficiency of his metabolism. Intravenous dextrose given under these circumstances will stimulate insulin production, inhibit lipolysis and increase requirements for gluconeogenesis. Some patients with severe gastrointestinal disease and an inadequate remnant of the remaining small intestine have been managed for years with TPN. Patients with acute hypercatabolic states are most often apparent in the intensive care unit, suffering from multiple trauma, septicaemia and multi-organ failure. There is no possibility that adequate calories can be given orally in these circumstances. In the postoperative period, if complications such as paralytic ilieus, peritonitis or fistulae occur and are unlikely to resolve after 3–4 days, then TPN should be commenced.

Team approach to TPN

If the decision to undertake TPN has been taken, there is no doubt that this is best undertaken by a team of people. Such a team will include a pharmacist, an intensive care doctor, bacteriologist, a member of the nursing staff and perhaps a biochemist. Such an approach reduces the rate of complications, in particular that of catheter-related sepsis by meticulous attention to detail.

It is not uncommon for a request to start total parenteral nutrition to be made for a patient in which the clinical situation is already complex, confused and often calamitous. The patient may already have bizarre fluid balance problems, oedema and wasting. The following factors should be corrected before TPN is started:

1 Low blood volume.
2 Extreme hypoalbuminaemia.
3 Low body temperature.
4 Pain and anxiety, which will worsen the stress response to trauma.

ASSESSMENT OF REQUIREMENTS

Far more important than deciding which fluid to give, is an accurate assessment of the patient's energy requirements and current nitrogen loss.

Table 12.4 Calculations of requirements.

Energy

Minimum 30 cal kg^{-1} daily
Additional postoperative complications 40–45 cal kg^{-1} daily
Hypercatabolism — in severe sepsis or burns requirements may reach
    50–60 cal kg^{-1} daily

These requirements are increased by 12% per °C fever

Nitrogen

This is calculated from losses:
Urine: 24 hour urine urea (mmol) $\times$ 0.035 = N_2 output in g
    + measured proteinuria (divide by 6.25 to convert to g N_2)
Other loss:
    Total sweat and stool losses = 1.6 g daily at normal
        temperature
    Fever: add 0.8 g $°C^{-1}$ daily
    Gastrointestinal losses: if not measured, estimate
        2–4 g N_2 l^{-1} of measured loss

Fluid losses in excess of 100 ml daily should have nitrogen and electrolyte contents measured, since estimation may be extremely inaccurate in these circumstances.

Evaluation of urine urea nitrogen

Urinary urea nitrogen will be 3–8 g with the patient taking no protein or amino acids and indicates mild skeletal muscle turnover. 8–13 g is equivalent to moderate muscle breakdown and greater than 13 g implies severe muscle breakdown.

Administration

Many of the fluids used in a parenteral nutrition regime are hypertonic and hence irritant to veins. Fat emulsion, however, are isotonic and may be infused into peripheral veins. Infusion of hypertonic carbohydrate and amino acid solutions should be into a central vein.

Insertion of the central venous line

The central venous line should be inserted under full aseptic surgical technique, preferably by the infraclavicular approach to the subclavian vein. The best material for the central venous line is silicone. This is non-irritant, does not encourage the formation of fibrin and may be left *in situ* for months in the absence of signs of infection. Whatever type of catheter is used it should be inserted in the operating theatre. The line is connected via a system of taps to the solutions for TPN, using Luer lock connections. It is essential that this line is dedicated to TPN. Drugs and blood should be administered via an alternative peripheral line. The position of the catheter should be always be checked by a chest x-ray, which will also demonstrate any pneumothorax produced by insertion.

Solutions available for TPN

Energy substrates

CARBOHYDRATES

In the United Kingdom at present the only carbohydrate which can be recommended is dextrose. Highly concentrated solutions are necessary to provide an adequate calorie intake. Fructose is only partially metabolised by an insulin independent pathway and sorbitol may produce metabolic acidosis. Frequently the critically ill patient may be hyperglycaemic already, with insulin resistance and considerable quantities of exogenous insulin may be required to facilitate the uptake and metabolism of the infused dextrose.

FAT

There is at present only one fat preparation suitable for TPN. This is the emulsion of soya bean oil, Intralipid. Its globules are identical with chylomicrons and are dealt with in the same way. Intralipid supplies essential fatty acids, phospholipids and glycerol in a solution of high calorific value. The total amount of fat delivered daily should be limited to 2 g kg^{-1}. This preparation is particularly useful where energy requirements are high since fat supplies 9 cal g^{-1}.

Fat globules may accumulate within the reticuloendothelial system decreasing antibody production and within the lungs with a possible increase in alveolar to arterial oxygen tension difference. In gram negative septicaemia, endotoxin inhibits the utilisation of fat. Recent evidence from premature babies shows that Intralipid in less than the recommended maximum dose accumulates in the lung, engorging capillaries and exacerbating ventilation perfusion inequality. This occurs in the absence of a lipaemic plasma. There is also evidence of impaired resistance to infection. Therefore, in small babies the disadvantages in Intralipid outweigh the advantages.

Intralipid should be stored in a refrigerator and removed 30 minutes prior to infusion. Administration of 500 units of heparin in each bottle will facilitate fat usage. No additives should be made to Intralipid as the emulsion may be thereby broken down. The exception to this is the addition of Vitilipid which contains fat soluble vitamins.

Comparison of glucose and fat as a calorie source

In fasting man receiving no protein, fat has no effect on nitrogen excretion but administration of carbohydrate reduces the nitrogen loss. This effect is maximal at a carbohydrate intake of 100 g daily. Therefore 100 g carbohydrate reduces gluconeogenesis whereas fat cannot do this. If however protein intake is adequate then carbohydrate and fat have the same effect on nitrogen excretion. In hypercatabolism infused fat prevents the breakdown of endogenous fat, not the breakdown of muscle, whereas a combination of glucose with insulin will inhibit muscle protein breakdown. If therefore a patient is excreting more than 15 g of nitrogen daily glucose is the preferred calorie source and insulin will probably be beneficial. Insulin also enhances the activity of the sodium pump, increasing both Na excretion and K retention. However, Intralipid has a number of advantages over carbohydrate. It is isotonic and can therefore be infused into peripheral veins. It contains essential fatty acids and phospholipids and can act as a vehicle for Vitilipid. The respiratory quotient of carbohydrate is 1, whereas that of fat is 0.7. Thus, fat increases CO_2 production less than does carbohydrate which may be important in patients is respiratory failure but it is much more expensive.

The best regimes are based on carbohydrate as the main energy source and use 500–1000 ml Intralipid twice weekly or more often if energy requirements are particularly high, for example in burns.

Table 12.5 Osmolality of plasma and some infusion solutions.

	mosmol kg^{-1}
Plasma	290
0.9% NaCl	308
10% Fat emulsion (Intralipid)	280
20% Fat emulsion (Intralipid)	330
5% Glucose	278
10% Glucose	523
20% Glucose	1250
30% Glucose	2100
50% Glucose	3800

Dextrose

Dextrose supplies 4 calories g^{-1}. Administration of more than 0.5 g kg^{-1} hour^{-1} dextrose in health results in hyperglycaemia and osmotic diuresis. Simple dextrose solutions are available in concentrations of 10, 20, 40 and 50% solutions. Alternatively solutions are available containing dextrose with electrolytes. An example of this is Glucoplex. Glucoplex 1000 contains 1000 calories l^{-1}. Glucoplex 1600 contains 1600 calories l^{-1}. These both contain, in addition,

Na   50 mmol l^{-1}
K   30 mmol l^{-1}
H$_2$PO$_4$^{3} 18 mmol l^{-1}
Mg   2.5 mmol l^{-1}
Cl   67 mmol l^{-1}
zinc   45.6 micromol l^{-1}

The osmolality of Glucoplex 1000 is 1500 mosmol kg^{-1}, that of Glucoplex 1600 is 2400 mosmol kg^{-1}.

Intralipid

This is available as a 10 or 20% solution, containing 100 or 200 g soya bean oil respectively, 12 g egg yolk phospholipids and 25 g of glycerol in each litre. Oxidation of fat supplies 9 calories g^{-1}.

Sources of nitrogen

The best solutions are those containing a balanced mixture of crystalline L amino acids. These solutions must be administered concurrently with an energy substrate to ensure that the amino acids are used for anabolism. Whatever solution is used, at least 25% of the amino acids should be essential.

Table 12.6   Essential amino acids.

Isoleucine
Leucine
Lysine
Valine
Methionine
Phenylalanine
Threonine
Tryptophan

In special circumstances certain other amino acids are essential. Ariginine is required for optimal utilisation of amino acid mixtures, cystine, cysteine for the foetus and histidine for infants and in renal failure. The Vamin series of amino acid solutions (Kabi Vitrum) currently contain 9.4 g l^{-1} nitrogen. In addition, these solutions contains:

Na 50 mmol l^{-1}
K 20 mmol l^{-1}
Ca 2.5 mmol l^{-1}
Mg 1.5 mmol l^{-1}
Cl 55 mmol l^{-1}

The disadvantage of these solutions is the relatively low nitrogen concentration which is a problem in the hypercatabolic patient, in whom fluid restriction is appropriate. The Synthamin series of amino acid solutions (Travenol) contain varying amounts of protein and the disadvantage of a rather high glycine content which may lead to hyperammonaemia and metabolic acidosis. Aminoplex 12 and 14 (Geistlich) contain 12 or 14 g l^{-1} nitrogen respectively. In addition the electrolyte content is:

Na 35 mmol l^{-1}
K 30 mmol l^{-1}
Mg 2.5 mmol l^{-1}
Cl 6–7 mmol l^{-1}
acetate 5 mmol l^{-1}

Aminoplex has an osmolality of 840 mosmol kg^{-1} with a pH of 7.4.

Relation between calorie and nitrogen requirements

Values between 150 and 200 cal g^{-1} of nitrogen have been recommended. However, it has been shown that the calorie requirement varies with the degree of catabolism. Table 12.7 shows the relationship between energy and nitrogen requirements.

Table 12.7 Energy and N_2 requirements.

	Starving	Catabolic	Hyper-catabolic
N_2 (g 24 hour^{-1}) requirements for equilibrium	7.5	14	25
kcal (total including protein)	2000	3000	4000
Non-protein calorie to N_2 ratio	250	200	135

Insulin

Insulin will be required in most regimes where high concentrations of dextrose are given for TPN. There are two possible ways of administering insulin:

1 Insulin may be added to the solution of dextrose when a variable amount of it will be adsorbed onto the glass or plastic of the container and the giving system. There is, however, an advantage with this system, in that should the infusion of dextrose stop so would administration of insulin and dangerous hypoglycaemia may be averted.

2 Insulin is given via a separate continuous infusion, for example in a syringe pump at the rate of 0.5 units of soluble insulin hourly initially. The disadvantage of this technique is that should the dextrose infusion stop there is a danger of profound hypoglycaemia. It no longer seems important when using concentrated insulin to make this up into albumin or haemaccel. Whichever method of administration of insulin is used blood sugar must be monitored frequently and the insulin dosage adjusted accordingly. A convenient repeatable method of glucose estimation utilises the glucose oxidase reaction in a portable machine such as the Reflomat which can be operated by nursing or medical staff on the ward.

Water

Maintenance water requirements are 30–35 ml kg^{-1} daily. It must be remembered that metabolism of solutions for TPN will produce carbon dioxide (CO_2) and water so this must be taken into account in the calculation of fluid balance. Water of metabolism amounts approximately to 1 ml for each calorie of energy supplied. Water requirements are dealt with in Chapters 1 and 5.

Most feeding regimes therefore require the simultaneous infusion of at least two bottles of fluid (one source of energy and one source of nitrogen). To keep mixing to a minimum these should be joined together as close to the patient as possible by a system of taps. In this way there is minimal interaction of fat with other nutrients and less likelihood of breaking down the emulsion.

These allowances cover resting metabolism, some physical activity and specific dynamic action but not increased needs due to burns, etc.

Table 12.8 Recommended allowances of nutritional substances.

	Allowances kg^{-1} daily body wt. to adults	
Water	30	ml
Energy	30	kcal = 0.13 MJ
Amino acid nitrogen	90	mg (0.7 g amino acids)
Glucose	2	g
Fat	2	g
Sodium	1–1.4	mmol
Potassium	0.7–0.9	mmol
Calcium	0.11	mmol
Magnesium	0.04	mmol
Iron	1	μmol
Manganese	0.6	μmol
Zinc	0.3	μmol
Copper	0.07	μmol
Chlorine	1.3–1.9	mmol
Phosphorus	0.15	mmol
Fluorine	0.7	μmol
Iodine	0.015	μmol
Thiamine	0.02	mg
Riboflavine	0.03	mg
Nicotinamide	0.2	mg
Pyridoxine	0.03	mg
Folic acid	3	μg
Cyanocobalamin	0.03	μg
Pantothenic acid	0.2	mg
Biotin	5	μg
Ascorbic acid	0.5	mg
Retinol	10	μg
Ergocalciferol or cholecalciferol	0.04	mg
Phytylmenaquinone	2	μg
α– Tocopherol	1.5	mg

Mineral requirements

Sodium

Average sodium requirements are 1 mmol kg^{-1} over 24 hours. Many patients have problems of Na retention with secondary hyper-aldosteronism and will require less than this.

Potassium

Potassium requirements are very variable, depending upon renal losses, insulin and glucose administration and are guided by daily urinary and plasma electrolyte measurements. When anabolism begins about 6 mmol of K per g of nitrogen will be required as the potassium enters the cell.

Calcium

Initially immobilisation makes calcium administration unnecessary. Measurement of plasma calcium should always take plasma albumin levels into account. Requirements in the long-term are about 0.11 mmol kg^{-1} daily.

Magnesium

No additional magnesium will be necessary if Glucoplex and Aminoplex solutions are used. Requirements are 0.04 mmol kg^{-1} over 24 hours. A solution of magnesium sulphate is available.

Phosphate

The requirements are 0.5 to 0.7 mmol kg^{-1} over 24 hours. In the acute situation at least 30 mmol of phosphate should be supplied daily. Sources of phosphate:
1 K_2HPO_4. This contains 20 mmol of potassium and 10 mmol of phosphate in 10 ml. This is a useful solution since in circumstances of hypophosphataemia the plasma K may also be low.
2 A sodium phosphate solution is available which contains Na 162 mmol l^{-1} K 19 mmol l^{-1} and phosphate 100 mmol l^{-1}.

Zinc

Requirements are 0.3 μ mol kg^{-1} daily. In the acute situation 20–40 μ mol should be administered daily. A solution of zinc sulphate is available.

Vitamins

Deficiency of any vitamin may occur if these are not replaced. Over enthusiastic replacement however will result in hypervitaminosis. A number of preparations of water soluble vitamins are available. The best one currently on the market would seem to be Solivito.

Table 12.9 Composition of a Solivito ampoule.

Vitamin B_1	1.2	mg
Vitamin B_2	1.8	mg
Nicotinamide	10	mg
Vitamin B_6	2	mg
Pantothenic acid	10	mg
Biotin	0.3	mg
Folic acid	0.2	mg
Vitamin B_{12}	2	μg
Vitamin C	30	mg

One ampoule of Solivito administered daily, diluted in a dextrose solution will cover basal daily requirements of water soluble vitamins. Alternative preparations include Parenterovite and Multibionta. Fat soluble vitamins may be convenietly given as Vitilipid 1 ampoule, 10 ml, in a bottle of Intralipid.

Table 12.10 Composition of a Vitilipid ampoule.

Retinol	75	μg (250 iu)
Calciferol	0.3	μg (12 iu)
Phytomenadione	15	μg
Fract. soybean oil	100	mg
Fract. egg phospholipids	12	mg
Glycerol	25	mg
NaOH to pH	8	

Folate should be given regularly as reports of folic acid deficiency during TPN are common. 10 mg folic acid intramuscularly on alternate days is a suitable dose. Vitamin B12 (1000 μg) is required intramuscularly weekly. If obstructive jaundice is present intravenous vitamin K_1 may be indicated. Parenteral iron may also be required.

Trace elements

A preparation of trace elements, Addamel 10 ml is available but it does involve duplication of certain additives with some regimes.

Table 12.11 Composition of an Addamel ampoule.

5	mmol Ca
1.5	mmol Mg
50	μmol ferric iron
20	μmol Zn
40	μmol manganese
5	μmol copper
50	μ fluoride
1	μ iodide
13.3	mmol chloride

No additives should be made to bottles unless absolutely necessary, because of the risk of contamination and infection. Additives are best mixed in the hospital pharmacy under conditions of laminar flow. The compatability of additives should always be checked with the pharmacy prior to mixing. Elimination of the need for additives is one of the chief advantages of premixed solutions.

HAZARDS OF PARENTERAL NUTRITION

Infection

Solutions for TPN make excellent culture media and additives provide a source of contamination. The infusion catheter can become contaminated and identical organisms grown from the blood stream and the catheter tip. The practice of tunnelling the central line so that the catheter lies under the skin for 10 cm before entering the vein has been tried to reduce the risk of sepsis. Patients at high risk are those with a tracheostomy and a subclavian central venous line. It is essential that the central line is dedicated to parenteral nutrition and that no drugs or blood products are infused through the same line. With the team approach to parenteral nutrition the catheter sepsis rate may be reduced to 4%.

Septicaemia is usually due to Gram positive or negative organisms but in patients previously treated with antibiotics *Candida albicans* may be responsible. Diagnosis of septicaemia is difficult as fever in these ill patients may be due to factors other than catheter sepsis for example blood transfusion. If infection is suspected a blood culture must be taken and all possible contaminated sites must be swabbed for culture. If the temperature returns to normal for at least 12 hours it is unnecessary to discontinue TPN. However, if fever persists and the source of infection is not located then the central venous line must be removed and sent for culture. Thereafter the entire administration system must be changed.

Biochemical disturbances

Hyperosmolality

This is commonly related to hyperglycaemia due to inadequate insulin administration. Blood sugar and osmolality should be monitored regularly as hyperglycaemia will produce an osmotic diuresis with the possibility of severe dehydration.

Rebound hypoglycaemia

When hypertonic dextrose solutions are discontinued 5% dextrose should be administered to prevent rebound hypoglycaemia.

Hypophosphataemia

Inadequate administration of phosphate results in weakness, tremors, and bone pain initially and later a reduction in cardiac output and coma. 2,3, DPG levels fall resulting in a shift of the oxygen dissociation curve to the left with consequent reduction in oxygen availability to the tissues. Reduction in ATP results in impaired membrane function with rigidity of red blood cells and reduced platelet survival. Tissue perfusion is impaired. Blood samples for phosphate estimation should not be taken whilst a dextrose infusion is in progress.

Hypokalaemia and hypomagnesaemia

These are discussed fully elsewhere in the book (see Chapters 7 and 8).

Metabolic acidosis

Administration or production of large amounts of acidic compounds will result in metabolic acidosis some relevant causes of which are listed below.

CAUSES OF METABOLIC ACIDOSIS

1 Excess cationic amino acids, for example, lysine, arginine.
2 High titratable acid of some amino acid solutions.
3 Metabolism of phosphate and sulphate radicals.
4 Lactic acidosis due to sorbitol or fructose administration.
5 Hyperammonaemia following metabolism of excess glycine.
6 Formation of ketone bodies from fat emulsions.
7 Poor peripheral tissue perfusion.

Deficiency states

Deficiency of almost any normal food substance may occur. This is particularly so with vitamins and trace elements. It is equally important to guard against excessive doses of vitamins. With regard to trace elements, low plasma levels of copper or caeruloplasmin are reliable indicators of copper deficiency. On the other hand, the plasma level of zinc varies with non specific factors such as infection and other stress and is therefore a poor indicator of total body zinc. Zinc deficiency is characterised by diarrhoea, depression, alopecia, dermatitis, impaired wound healing and reduction in taste and smell. Some patients are particularly prone to develop zinc deficiency, for example those with cirrhosis, those on long term steroids and folowing adrenalectomy. Cobolt is essential for the production of vitamin B12, chromium may be important in glucose tolerance; manganese, molybdenum and selenium are also important.

Essential fatty acid deficiency

Fatty acids are important for cell membrane structure and function. Deficiency causes increased susceptibility to infection, pruritis, diarrhoea and anaemia. An eczematous skin rash appears and fatty infiltration of the liver with an increase in transaminases occurs. There is increased platelet aggregation. The essential fatty acids are:

1 Linoleic.
2 Linolenic.
3 Arachidonic.

In adult man linoleic acid alone may be sufficient to prevent deficiency. Daily requirements are 25–100 mg kg^{-1} although this is higher in illness. Intralipid contains 55 g of linoleic and 8 g of linolenic acid in each 500 ml of a 20% solution. Alternative ways of giving fatty acids are:

1 Oral ingestion of oils with a high linoleic acid content (Naudicelle capsules).
2 Topical application of 2–3 mg kg^{-1} daily of linoleic acid to the skin.

Jaundice

Fatty liver has been described in some patients receiving TPN using only dextrose and amino acid solutions and this may be improved by administration of fat. Liver enzymes may rise during TPN and some workers have observed intrahepatic cholestasis. There may be some dangers therefore in TPN in patients with known liver disease. It has been shown that in some forms of hepatic failure infusion of branched chain amino acids may improve the hepatic coma, whereas, high concentrations of aromatic amino acids can precipitate encephalopathy.

Hypoalbuminaemia

This is very common in critically ill patients, leading to impaired healing, reduced resistance to infection and maldistribution of water between body fluid compartments. Unfortunately albumin administered intravenously is rapidly broken down in the hypercatabolic patient. Therefore to restore plasma albumin to normal will require 25–75 g albumin daily either as HPPF (see Chapter 10) or salt poor albumin which is extremely expensive.

Excess body sodium

Salt overload or retention in these patients may be due to a number of factors:

1 An excessive sodium load may be given.
2 A reduction in plasma albumin leads to a reduction in effective circulating blood volume and secondary hyperaldosteronism.
3 Intermittent positive pressure ventilation and positive end expiratory pressure.
4 The stress response to trauma.
5 Renal failure.
6 Infection.

Other complications

Other complications include lethargy, allergic reactions (rare), muscle cramps and pain, tachycardia, flushing, headache, nausea and vomiting, dehydration, fever, alopecia and anaemia. Glutamic acid in susceptible individuals produces a syndrome similar to monosodium glutamate sensitivity.

MONITORING

Daily

Until the patient becomes stable on a TPN regime the following monitoring should be carried out daily:
1 Weight.
2 Plasma urea and electrolyte concentrations.
3 Blood glucose — this should be estimated 2 hourly on the ward until the patient is stable.
4 Full blood count.
5 Accurate fluid balance chart.
6 24 hour urinary urea and electrolyte concentrations.
7 Blood gases.
   Following stability the frequency of these investigations can be markedly reduced. In the initial evaluation plasma should be examined 12 hours after the completion of an Intralipid infusion to ensure that the fat is being utilised. A heparinised blood sample is allowed to stand and the plasma examined for opalescent fat globules.

Twice weekly monitoring

1 Liver function tests.
2 Plasma proteins.
3 Prothrombin time.
4 Plasma and urine osmolality.
5 Ca, Mg and PO₄ concentration.

A flow chart is necessary to follow progress. Nutritional assessment should be repeated regularly.

SAMPLE REGIMES

Sample basic regime

Glucoplex 1600, 2 litres over 24 hours (line 1).
Aminoplex 12, 1 litre over 24 hours (line 2).

This will provide 12.44 g of nitrogen and 3200 calories in 3 litres of fluid. The Na content of this is 135 mmol, K 90 mmol, Mg 7.5 mmol, zinc 91.2 μmol and phosphate 36 mmol. It provides 260 calories per gram of nitrogen and 7 mmol of K per gram of nitrogen. In the more hypercatabolic patient in whom fluid balance is not a problem an increased amount of amino acid solution may be give remembering to give adequate calorie cover (see Table 12.2). If Na restriction is indicated plain dextrose would be preferable to Glucoplex remembering to add zinc, K and PO₄. Twice weekly or more often Intralipid should be substituted for dextrose (Glucoplex) as previously discussed. TPN may be used for patients in renal failure, water retention being corrected during dialysis. Amino acid solutions should not be given whilst dialysis is in progress as it will be lost across the membrane.

FAILURE TO INDUCE ANABOLISM

This may simply be due to the fact that the patient is extremely hypercatabolic or due to inadequate insulin administration. Mobilisation of the patient is beneficial. It encourages an increase in lean body mass rather than an increase in fat production. It may take several weeks for TPN to have an effect on plasma albumin.

HOME TPN

This is increasingly practised in the USA. The patient is trained to change his own TPN nutrient bottles and is supplied with a syringe pump to regulate the rate of administration.

CHANGE TO ORAL INTAKE

This should be undertaken slowly. There may initially be a lack of appetite hence TPN should be tailed off rather than stopped abruptly. Diarrhoea may occur due to disaccharide deficiency. If a nasogastric tube is required for enteral feeding a fine bore tube should be used. These have a diameter of only 1 mm and are inserted with a wire introducer. They are much more comfortable for the patient and allow him to swallow with ease if he is able to do so. They are not associated with the high incidence of stricture and erosion that larger Ryle's tubes are. The position of the tube in the stomach should always be confirmed by x-ray since cannulation of the bronchial tree is not uncommon.

ENTERAL NUTRITION

Oral or nasogastric feeding should always be the route of choice for feeding patients. Sometimes enteral feeding can be accomplished by a feeding jejunostomy fashioned during the course of surgery for upper gastrointestinal tract pathology. Whole protein can be readily absorbed. Although preparations of free amino acids and oligopeptides are available (elemental diets) these are only indicated in cases of severe pancreatic insufficiency or short bowel syndrome.

Postoperatively gastric stasis is not uncommon but early feeding can be started via a tube positioned in the duodenum or the jejunum.

If large volumes of feeds are given as a bolus injection nausea and diarrhoea may occur. Continuous gravity feeding overcomes this to some extent and uses less nursing time. In particularly difficult cases enteral feeds may be administered by a continuous infusion pump. Diarrhoea can also be prevented by introducing the feed slowly in a dilute form. Other causes of diarrhoea should be sought and if none is found codein phosphate or loperamide may be used for symptomatic treatment. There are now many commercially available enteral feeds. These have a great advantage over liquidised feeds in that they arrive in a sterile container whereas liquidised food has been found to be heavily contaminated with organisms such as *Klebsiella*. The gastric contents of ill patients are not always sterile as in health and with reduced resistance to infection pathogenic organisms are often found in the stomach.

One commonly used preparation is Clinifeed 400 which has an osmolality of 330 mosmol kg^{-1}, and a nonprotein calorie to nitrogen ration 142:1 and is suitabe for the vast majority of patients.

Regardless of the route of administration of nutrition it is only meticulous attention to detail which will produce success and freedom from complications.

Chapter 13
Acid Base Balance

In a neutral solution there are equal numbers of hydrogen (H) ions and hydroxyl (OH) ions. An acid solution contains an excess of H and an alkaline solution an excess of OH ions.

pH is the negative logarithm to the base 10 of the H ion concentration. The pH scale indicates the number of H ions logarithmically.

Pure distilled water contains 0.000 0001 mol l⁻¹ H ions and the same number of OH ions. Therefore the log to the base 10 of 0.000 0001 being −7 the product of the H and OH ions in pure water is −14. In the pH range 0–14 an increase in H ion concentration and increased acidity results in a falling pH.

Because this scale in logarithmic each unit change in pH is equivalent to a 10-fold change in H ion concentration.

(pH)		(nmol⁻¹)
6.8 is equivalent to a H ion concentration of		160
7.1	⟶	80
7.4	⟶	40
7.7	⟶	20

(1 Nanomole $= 10^{-9}$ mole.)

The normal pH range of the body is 7.35–7.45 and this is slightly alkaline.

Normal H ion concentration is 35–45 nmol l⁻¹.

An acid is a proton donor or H ion donor.

A base is a proton acceptor or H ion acceptor.

Acidaemia occurs when arterial blood pH is less than 7.36 or H ion concentration is greater than 44 nmol l⁻¹.

Alkalaemia occurs when pH is greater than 7.44 or H ion concentration is less than 36 nmol l⁻¹.

Acidosis and alkalosis are abnormal conditions which cause acidaemia and alkalaemia respectively *if* no secondary changes occur to compensate for the primary change. Although there are wide variations in daily acid and base intake there is no specific centre for H ion regulation.

Most physiological processes involve enzymatic activity which is optimal around the H ion concentration of body fluids. This influence is much more important than temperature or concentration of substrates. The fundamental problem for humans lies in the fact that cells produce large amounts of H ions during metabolism.

Table 13.1 Daily hydrogen ion balance (mmol day^{-1}).

Input		Output	
Volatile			
CO_2	13 000	Lungs	13 000
Lactate	1500	Liver/ kidney	1500
Non-volatile			
Protein, SO_4, PO_4	45	Titratable acid	30
Phospholipid	13	NH_4	40
Other	12		

Metabolism of carbohydrate fat and protein results in CO_2 production.

$$C_6H_{12}O_6 \; + \; 6O_2 \; = \; 6CO_2 \; + \; 6H_2O$$
$$\text{Glucose} \qquad \text{Oxygen}$$

The CO_2 then reacts with water to form H ions

$$CO_2 + H_2O \rightleftharpoons H_2CO_3 \rightleftharpoons H^+ + HCO_3$$

Despite this reaction the H ion concentration is normally kept within strict limits by two mechanisms:
1 Buffering of the H ions.
2 Elimination of the H ions.

BUFFERING

The law of mass action states that in any chemical reaction at equilibrium $HA \rightleftharpoons H^+ + A$—where A is any anion and HA is undissociated acid. This may be written in an alternative form where K is the dissociation constant of the reaction and [] is concentration.

$$K = \frac{[H] + [A]}{[HA]} \quad \text{or} \quad [H] = \frac{K\,[HA]}{[A]}$$

The negative logarithm of this equation gives the Henderson Hasselbalch equation.

$$pH = pK + \log \frac{[A]}{[HA]} \qquad (1)$$

The combination of a weak acid and a strong base or a strong acid and a weak base constitutes a buffer solution into which addition of H or OH ions has little effect on the pH of the solution. In plasma and tissue fluid three buffer systems exist.

1   Proteins. $H^+ + Prot^- \rightleftharpoons HProt$
2   Phosphate. $H^+ + HPO_4^- \rightleftharpoons H_2PO_4$
3   Carbonic acid, bicarbonate. $H^+ + HCO_3 \rightleftharpoons H_2CO_3 \rightleftharpoons CO_2 + H_2O$

Within red blood cells haemoglobin forms an additional important buffering system. This is discussed below.

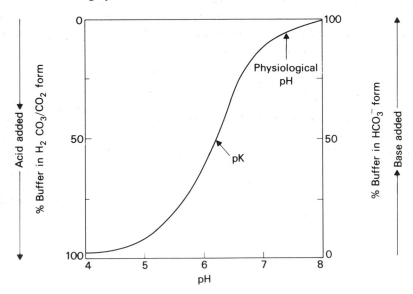

Fig. 13.1 The reaction curve for a buffer system.

Each buffer system has a pK value at which its buffering capacity is maximal. K is the dissociation constant of the reaction and pK is the negative logarithm to the base 10 of the dissociation constant. Most buffering occurs within $\pm$ 1 pH unit of the pK value of the system. Fig. 13.1 shows the curve for the bicarbonate system which is most effective at pK 6.2. At plasma pH 7.4 therefore this system is relatively ineffective.

Blood buffering systems

Table 13.2   Constituents of total blood buffering capacity

	%Total buffering capacity
Plasma	
Bicarbonate	65
Phosphate	1
Protein	5
Erythrocytes	
Haemoglobin	29

Bicarbonate carbonic acid

This is the main buffer system in blood. The relation between bicarbonate and carbonic acid concentration is 20:1. Its pK value is 6.1 and therefore its chemical buffering capacity at pH 7.4 is poor but its efficiency increases when blood pH decreases. This is an open ended system because CO_2 can be adjusted immediately by ventilation in normal lungs and HCO_3 by the kidney in the longer term. The large amount of plasma HCO_3 available (24–28 mmol l^{-1}) makes this system especially important.

Phosphate

This system has a pK of 6.8 and is therefore a better chemical buffer than the bicarbonate system but its concentration in plasma is much lower and therefore its capacity as a buffer is much less although it is important in urine and ICF.

Haemoglobin and protein

All proteins have a number of titratable groups within their molecular structure with ability to buffer pH changes. In haemoglobin this is due to the imidazole group of histidine which dissociates less in oxygenated than deoxygenated blood. Haemoglobin has three times the buffering capacity of plasma proteins gram for gram and twice the concentration therefore it has six times the total buffering capacity of plasma proteins.

In summary buffering is the mechanism by which an influx of H ions is initially dealt with by the body and limits the change in pH. Thereafter respiratory mechanisms become active to eliminate CO_2 and later renal regulation of acid secretion restores buffer capacity. If the plasma proteins or HCO_3 concentration are decreased the buffer capacity of the plasma will be reduced and an acid load will raise the H ion concentration more than usual.

ELIMINATION OF HYDROGEN ION

Rapid elimination, respiratory response

Oxidation of energy substrates produces CO_2 which can be eliminated by the lungs. Arterial CO_2 varies directly with CO_2 production and inversely with alveolar ventilation. CO_2 readily diffuses across cell membranes producing changes in pH in both ICF and ECF. In the normal situation increased CO_2 production stimulates respiration and can be matched by increased alveolar elimination. Total ventilatory failure for 20 minutes produces a profound acidosis with an arterial P_{CO_2} of 14.7 kPa (110 mmHg), and pH 7.03 whereas renal failure for this length of time has no effect. The inefficiency of the carbonic acid bicarbonate chemical buffer system has already been discussed but carbonic acid is in equilibrium with dissolved CO_2 in body fluids and can therefore be eliminated through the lungs. Addition of H ions increases H_2CO_3 at the expense of a reduction in bicarbonate.

$$HCO_3^- + H^+ \rightleftharpoons H_2CO_3$$

more CO_2 is then formed;

$$H_2CO_3 \rightleftharpoons CO_2 + H_2O$$

Slow elimination, renal response

Long term control of H ion excretion depends on renal mechanisms. Excess H ions produced by the body are dealt with by the following mechanisms:

1 Buffers.
2 Formation of ammonia.
3 Reabsorption of filtered bicarbonate.

Buffers

20–30 mmol H ions are excreted daily by conversion of monohydrogen to dihydrogen phosphate. $H^+ + HPO_4^- \rightleftharpoons H_2PO_4$.

Formation of ammonia

NH_3 is formed in the tubular epithelium throughout the nephron. 60% is formed from glutamine by deamination and deamidation, 30–35% from free arterial NH_3. This NH_3 diffuses into the renal tubular lumen and binds a H ion to produce non-diffusible ammonium ion (NH_4^+) which is excreted. In this way 30–50 mmol H ions is excreted daily under normal circumstances and this may rise to 700 mmol daily in severe acidosis.

Reabsorption of filtered bicarbonate

85–90% of filtered HCO_3 is reabsorbed in the proximal tubule. The amount of HCO_3 reaching the distal nephron varies with the filtered load of HCO_3 and effective ECF volume. In the proximal tubule HCO_3 reabsorption occurs with H ion excretion. Carbonic anhydrase within renal tubular cells catalyses the hydration of CO_2 to carbonic acid which then ionises to H and HCO_3 ions. Reabsorption of HCO_3 occurs into the blood stream and H ions are excreted in the urine in exchange for Na ions. The increase in HCO_3 reabsorption by the distal renal tubule in acidosis is progressive and takes five

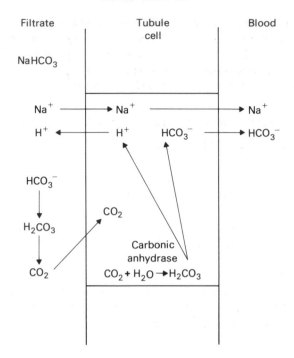

Fig. 13.2 Hydrogen ion excretion by the renal tubule.

days to reach maximal response when 700 mmol H ion can be excreted daily. In the absence of carbonic anhydrase for example when the diuretic acetazolamide (a carbonic anhydrase inhibitor) is given acid excretion is reduced, the urine becomes alkaline, large amounts of $NaHCO_3$ are excreted and plasma HCO_3 falls.

Factors affecting proximal tubular H ion excretion

1 Intracellular acid base status which in turn varies with arterial CO_2, metabolic H and K ion status.
2 Luminal pH.
3 Functional ECF volumes.
4 Availability of reabsorbable anions.
5 Carbonic anhydrase.
6 Parathormone.

Hypokalaemia enhances proximal tubular H ion secretion by increasing the availability of H ion to the secretory mechanism (see Chapter 3). If effective ECF volume is depleted the Na:H ion exchange mechanism permits retention of Na so that ECF volume is maintained at the expense of pH regulation.

Factors affecting distal tubular H ion excretion

1 Intracellular acid base state.
2 Luminal pH.
3 Mineralocorticoid activity and K status.

Hyperaldosteronism enhances distal Na reabsorption and H and K ion excretion.

In clinical practice the only effective measurement that can be made is that of ECF status. This is assessed from arterial blood gas analysis. In the acute situation however there is a very poor correlation between this and the intracellular pH. This is the case in hypokalaemia where an ECF alkalosis exists with an ICF acidosis. In K depletion H ions enter the cell to maintain electrical balance and replace the intracellular K.

MEASUREMENT OF ACID BASE BALANCE

A heparinised arterial blood sample is taken to measure pH, Pa_{CO_2} and HCO_3. The combined information is essential in the assessment of respiratory and metabolic disorders of acid base status.

Normal values

pH 7.36–7.44
Pa_{CO_2} 4.6–5.6 kPa (35–42 mmHg)
HCO_2 22–28 mmol l^{-1}

Standard bicarbonate

The standard bicarbonate is that value of HCO_3 measured in the plasma of fully oxygenated whole blood at a temperature of 37°C and Pa_{CO_2} 5.3 kPa (40 mmHg). It is therefore effectively an evaluation of the metabolic status only.

Base excess

This is the base concentration of whole blood measured by titration against a strong acid to pH 7.40 at a P_{CO_2} of 5.3 kPa (40 mmHg) at 37°C. For negative values (base deficit) titration is carried out with a strong base. Base excess is measured in mmol l^{-1} and is an attempt to quantify the excess or deficit of HCO_3. The normal range is -1 to $+2$ mmol l^{-1} and it represents residual buffering capacity.

Technique for blood sampling

The sampling syringe and needle should contain just enough heparin (100 units per ml) to fill the dead space. Excess or more concentrated heparin reduces the measured pH by virtue of its own acidity. Blood may be sampled by direct arterial puncture from the radial, brachial or femoral artery or withdrawn from an indwelling arterial cannula taking care to avoid air bubbles.

Measurement should be undertaken immediately since metabolism will continue within blood cells at room temperature thus increasing P_{aCO_2}. If this is impossible the sample should be stored on ice. Diffusion of CO_2 across the walls of plastic syringes does not produce a change in CO_2 tension within the first 3 hours of storage.

pH measurement

H ion concentration is measured by a glass electrode with a membrane which behaves as though it were permeable only to H ions and the derived pH is displayed on a meter. P_{CO_2} is measured by the Severinghaus electrode which incorporates a modification of this technique when a CO_2 permeable membrane is used.

Bicarbonate

This may be calculated by extrapolation from the pH and CO_2 using the Sigaard-Anderson (SA) nomogram.

This is effectively a graphic representation of the Henderson-Hasselbalch equation, in which pH is plotted against log P_{aCO_2}. Lines can be plotted on this nomogram showing the changes in pH which occur when a sample with a normal haemoglobin concentration is equilibrated with various concentrations of CO_2.

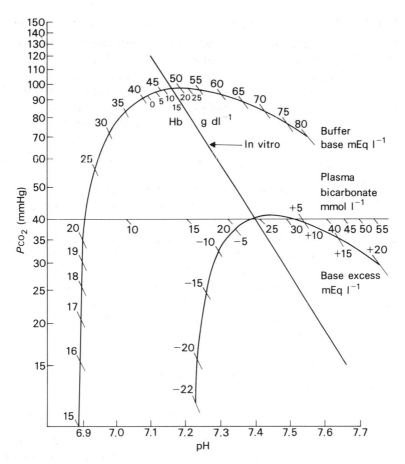

Fig. 13.3 pH, P_aCO_2 plot on Sigaard-Anderson nomogram. T = 37°C.

An arterial blood sample is taken and equilibrated with two gas mixtures containing different but known concentrations of CO_2 and the pH of the sample is measured. Two points are therefore plotted on the nomogram and joined by a straight line. This is called the buffer line and describes the relationship between pH and P_aCO_2 in that particular blood sample. The pH of the patients blood is measured anaerobically in the sample. Using this pH value and the buffer line the CO_2 of the sample can be interpolated from the nomogram.

The buffer line will cross the horizontal plasma bicarbonate line at a Pa_{CO_2} of 5.3 kPa (40 mmHg), where the bicarbonate value can be read. This is the standard bicarbonate.

The metabolic component of an acid base disorder may therefore be described by the standard bicarbonate which in effect is independent of the respiratory component. However base excess is a better parameter as it permits quantitative calculation of the dose of HCO_3 required for correction of the disturbance (see below).

If a primary disturbance occurs in the respiratory or metabolic mechanism for H ion excretion a compensatory change takes place in the other component to restore the pH towards normal but this never is complete and metabolic compensation takes about a week to become fully effective.

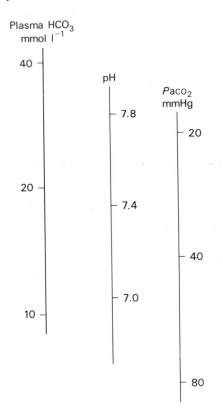

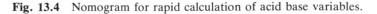

Fig. 13.4 Nomogram for rapid calculation of acid base variables.

Some simplified nomograms based on the Henderson-Hasselbalch equation permit calculation of a third variable when any two have already been measured.

Transcutaneous P_{CO_2}

CO_2 diffuses readily through body tissues and recently developed electrodes make it possible to monitor P_{CO_2} continuously noninvasively from the surface of the skin. The CO_2 sensor is based on the Severinghaus electrode. The skin must be heated under the surface of the electrode to produce capillary vasodilatation and arterialisation of the blood within. A correction factor is applied to allow for the increase in cutaneous P_{CO_2} due to the production of heat and to estimate Pa_{CO_2}. As this can provide continuous monitoring it is particularly useful to predict the onset of respiratory failure in patients not receiving ventilatory support.

DISTURBANCES OF ACID BASE BALANCE

In the management of patients with severe acid base disturbance it is essential to keep in mind the clinical condition of the patient when evaluating laboratory results. An isolated pH measurement is totally valueless without an arterial P_{CO_2} and in the case of respiratory disease a Pa_{O_2} as well. Free H ions are constantly being produced by the body but changes in H ion concentration are kept to minimum by buffering mechanisms as already discussed. Respiratory and renal compensatory mechanisms come into play when buffering capacity is exceeded in an attempt to achieve a normal plasma pH.

Classically disturbances of acid base balance are divided into respiratory or metabolic acidosis or alkalosis and may be considered in relation to the Henderson-Hasselbalch equation:

$$pH = pK + \log \frac{HCO_3^-}{H_2CO_3} \tag{1}$$

Normal plasma HCO_3 is 24 mmol l^{-1} and H_2CO_3 is 1.2 mmol l^{-1} so that

$$\log \frac{HCO_3^-}{H_2CO_3} = \log \frac{24}{1.2}$$

$$= \log 20 = 1.301$$

therefore $\quad pH = 6.1 + 1.301 = 7.40.$

Metabolic (non-respiratory) acidosis

This occurs when an abnormal amount of *non*-carbonic acid is formed or an abnormal loss of base occurs. Typical values are:

pH less than 7.36 (H ion concentration more than 44 mmol l^{-1})
PaCO$_2$ less than 4.6 kPa (35 mmHg)
HCO$_3$ less than 18 mmol l^{-1}

An increase in anion gap may occur (see below). In metabolic acidosis the value of $\log \frac{HCO_3}{H_2CO_3}$ will be reduced and hence pH falls.

Causes of metabolic acidosis

ACCUMULATION OF ACID

1 Diabetic ketoacidosis when blood levels of acetoacetate, acetone and betahydroxybutyrate are increased.
2 Lactic acidosis.
3 Renal failure when sulphate and phosphate radicles accumulate.
4 Salicylate overdose.
5 Following cardiac arrest. Anaerobic metabolism occurs in hypoxic situations and in conjunction with impaired tissue perfusion H ions are generated.

Substances such as paraldehyde, methyl alcohol, ethylene glycol, fructose, sorbitol, xylitol and ethanol may cause metabolic acidosis. There may also be an increase in H ion concentration from accumulated hydrochloric acid released during the metabolism of arginine and lysine in synthetic amino acid solutions and following the therapeutic use of ammonium chloride.

LOSS OF BICARBONATE

1 From the gastrointestinal tract:
(a) Small intestinal, pancreatic or biliary fistulae

(b)   Diarrhoea

(c)   Ureteroenterostomy

(d)   Cholestyramine.

2   From the kidney:

(a)   Renal tubular acidosis

(b)   Carbonic anhydrase inhibitors (Acetazolamide).

The body will try to compensate for this fall in pH by stimulation of respiration and a fall in $Paco_2$ which will return the pH towards normal by reduction in H_2CO_3. This is termed respiratory compensation. Although the fall in pH is modified it does not return completely to normal.

Clinical effects of acidosis

1   Decreased cardiac output.

2   Pulmonary hypertension.

3   Cardiac arrythmias and arrest.

4   Oliguria.

5   Increase in circulating catecholamines.

6   Mental changes.

Experimentally induced metabolic acidosis due to infusion of NH_4Cl produces the following disturbances of renal electrolyte transport.

1   Inhibition of Na reabsorption in the distal renal tubule independent of aldosterone or filtered Cl load or volume expansion. Thus Na excretion is increased without any change in GFR, renin or aldosterone and not due to volume expansion.

2   Even in the presence of a rise in plasma K the excretion of K is inhibited.

3   Tubular Ca reabsorption is inhibited. This effect is independent of changes in parathormone secretion.

Treatment of metabolic acidosis

Treatment is directed at the underlying cause, and much of this has already been discussed in other chapters. Therapy with $NaHCO_3$ should be reserved for fairly severe disorders since it is not without hazard.

SODIUM BICARBONATE (NaHCO₃)

NaHCO₃ solution is available in a variety of concentrations. That commonly used for resuscitation is 8.4% which contains 1 mmol ml⁻¹ of Na and HCO₃ and therefore there is a danger of the high Na load precipating heart failure. The solution is hypertonic and irritant to veins resulting in extensive skin necrosis if the solution leaks from the vein into the tissues. A hyperosmolality syndrome may be precipitated therefore 8.4% NaHCO₃ should be reserved for acute situations such as cardiac arrest, should preferably by given via a central line and in circumstances in which fluid restriction is appropriate.

Other disadvantages of NaHCO₃

1   In uncontrolled diabetes mellitus, acidosis exists with a low level of 2,3 DPG. Acidosis shifts the oxygen dissociation curve to the right and a low 2,3 DPG shifts it to the left so that the effect of these two abnormalities cancel each other out and oxygen delivery and tissue oxygenation remain normal. If NaHCO₃ is administered in these circumstances the pH will rise leaving the unopposed effect of a low 2,3 DPG to shift the oxygen dissociation curve to the left with impaired delivery of oxygen to the tissues. 2,3 DPG levels take several days to return to normal and it is important in this respect to ensure a normal plasma phosphate.

2   In diabetes NaHCO₃ may precipitate the disequilibrium syndrome. This is discussed in Chapter 14.

3   Rebound alkalosis may occur if excessive doses of NaHCO₃ are used.

4   Administration of NaHCO₃ results in a rise in Pa_{CO_2}. If the patient is able to hyperventilate the excess CO_2 can be excreted via the lungs. In patients with an impaired conscious level mechanical ventilation at a high minute volume may be required with repeated measurement of blood gas tensions.

5   In a hypokalaemic patient NaHCO₃ administration will increase pH, promote further K uptake into the cell and lethal hypokalaemia may occur.

In summary, NaHCO₃ is a dangerous drug but may be essential after cardiac arrest for the successful action of inotropic agents.

TRIHYDROXYMETHYLAMINOMETHANE (THAM)

THAM is a non-sodium containing buffer which has been used in some parts of the world with a variable degree of success to treat metabolic acidosis.

Lactic acidosis

Lactic acidosis may be broadly classified into type A where there is inadequate delivery of oxygen to the tissues and lactate is generated faster than it can be removed or type B where tissue hypoxia is not relevant.

Causes of type A lactic acidosis

1 Exercise.
2 Shock.
3 Hypoxia (Pa_{O_2} less than 35 mmHg).
4 Anaemia.

Causes of type B lactic acidosis

1 Drugs: phenformin, ethanol, paracetamol poisoning.
2 Intravenous feeding using excessive doses of sorbitol or fructose.
3 Diabetes.
4 Renal failure.
5 Liver disease.
6 Infection especially septicaemia.
7 Leukaemia, lymphoma.
8 Thiamine deficiency.
9 Hereditary: glucose-6-phosphatase deficiency.

The commonest cause of acute serious type B lactic acidosis is biguanide therapy for diabetes. Phenformin is ten times more likely than metformin to produce an attack of lactic acidosis (0.64 cases per 1000 patient years of treatment for phenformin compared to 0.05–0.08 for metformin). The mortality of type B acidosis is 50%.

Whenever possible an attack should be prevented. This involves abandoning phenformin in favour of metformin and using glucose rather than fructose or sorbitol as the energy substrate for parenteral nutrition. The danger with fructose infusion increases at an infusion rate greater than 0.5 g kg^{-1} hour^{-1}.

Treatment of lactic acidosis should be directed at the underlying cause ensuring adequate oxygen delivery to the tissues at all times. Alkalinisation with NaHCO$_3$ is the mainstay of therapy. Isotonic NaHCO$_3$ (1.4%) should be used to bring the pH back to normal over about 6 hours. Often over 1000 mmol bicarbonate may be required. If hyperkalaemia coexists this therapy will be beneficial as the K will enter the cells as the pH rises. If hypergly caemia exists insulin may be required.

A central venous pressure line and urinary catheter should be inserted to monitor progress as circulatory overload with cardiac failure is a serious complication. Haemodialysis may be required to treat cardiac failure. Repeated estimations of blood gases are essential in any disturbance of acid base balance and in these circumstances are of greater practical value than repeated lactate levels.

Metabolic (non-respiratory alkalosis)

This occurs due to excess production of base or abnormal loss of non-carbonic acid. Typical findings are:

pH greater than 7.44
Pa_{CO_2} greater than 6.0 kPa (45 mmHg)
H ion concentration less than 36 mmol l^{-1}
HCO$_3$ ion concentration greater than 32 mmol l^{-1}

In this situation the HCO$_3$ component in the Henderson-Hasselbalch equation (1) is increased, therefore log HCO$_3$$^-$ is increased and pH rises. Compensation occurs by hypoventilation so the H$_2$CO$_3$ also rises thereby modifying the increase in pH.

Causes of metabolic alkalosis

1   Loss of H ions.
Renal
    Primary and secondary hyperaldosteronism and K depletion.
    Conn's syndrome.
    Cushing's syndrome.
    Bartter's syndrome.
    ACTH secreting tumour.

Drugs
  diuretics — thiazides, frusemide, ethacrynic acid
  corticosteroids
  carbenoxolone.
Licquorice.
Post hypercapnoea.
Gastrointestinal
  Nasogastric suction
  Vomiting
  High intestinal obstruction.
  Villous adenoma.
  Congenital.
2 Gain in alkali.
  Iatrogenic milk alkali syndrome.
  Administration of $NaHCO_3$.
  Metabolic conversion of organic acid anions to HCO_3
      e.g. lactate and citrate.

This situation is seen after a large blood transfusion when the citrate is metabolised over the next 48 hours to HCO_3 resulting in metabolic alkalosis.

A metabolic alkalosis is perpetuated when there is a reduction in ECF volume, where excess mineralocorticoid activity occurs with K depletion especially when this becomes severe (greater than 450 mmol total body K deficit). In these situations renal excretion of HCO_3 is reduced. Metabolic alkalosis is almost always accompanied by a low chloride, which maintains electrical neutrality in the presence of a raised HCO_3.

Urine chloride

This will be low when hydrochloric acid is lost from the stomach, when intravenous $NaHCO_3$ or diuretics have been administered but high in hyperaldosteronism, Bartter's syndrome, Cushing's syndrome, licquorice ingestion and severe prolonged K deficiency. These disturbances are further discussed elsewhere.

Clinical effects of alkalosis

  Tetany.
  Hypocapnic vasoconstriction.

Left shift in oxygen dissociation curve.
Mental changes.
Hypokalaemia.

Kidney

In the proximal tubule there is obligatory Na reabsorption the extent of which is controlled by ECF volume. In the distal tubule Na is reabsorbed in exchange for K or H ion and influenced by aldosterone, such that if hypokalaemia occurs there will be increased H ion excretion. When renal retention of HCO_3 occurs correction of the pH alone without treatment of the underlying disease will result in recurrence and persistence of the metabolic alkalosis.

Treatment of metabolic alkalosis

Severe alkalosis may be life threatening especially if it is accompanied by hypokalaemia, but it is uncommon. Treatment includes the following:

1 Restoration of ECF volume. This may involve transfusion of NaCl, plasma or blood. It is important to give chloride, NaCl being simplest if a Na load is not contraindicated.
2 Restoration of plasma and whole body K concentration— using KCl or K conserving diuretics such as triamterene or amiloride if indicated.
3 Inhibition of aldosterone where appropriate, using spironolactone.
4 Inhibition of carbonic anhydrase by acetazolamide which will produce retention of H ions.
5 Direct acidification. HCl, NH_4Cl, lysine or arginine hydrochloride may be used. These may all be given intravenously and will result in the release of free H ions. HCl should only be administered through a central venous line at a rate of 0.2 mmol H kg^{-1} hour^{-1}. A maximum dose of $300-350$ mmol day^{-1} should not be exceeded.

Respiratory acidosis

$$pH = pK + \log \frac{HCO_3^-}{H_2CO_3} \tag{1}$$

This is due to an excess of CO_2 and may be acute or chronic; in the latter situation renal compensation occurs. CO_2 becomes hydrated to H_2CO_3 so that the value log HCO_3^- falls with a fall in pH. The kidney compensates by retaining HCO_3 so reducing the fall in pH.

Causes of respiratory acidosis

1 Chronic obstructive pulmonary disease (COPD).
2 Respiratory centre depression, for example, narcotic analgesic overdose.
3 Impaired neuromuscular function:
  Neuromuscular blocking drugs myasthenia gravis.
4 Excess CO_2 in inspired gas mixtures. This is only likely to occur during anaesthesia with malfunctioning apparatus.
5 In creased CO_2 production — fever, oxidation of the concentrated dextrose solutions used for energy substrates during parenteral nutrition.
6 Restrictive chest wall or lung disease.
7 Adult respiratory distress syndrome in its later stages. Typical blood gases in the acute situation of respiratory depression are as follows:

pH   7.2
Pa_{CO_2} 9.46 kPa (70 mmHg)
Pa_{O_2} 9.46 kPa (70 mmHg)
HCO_3 29 mmol l^{-1}

In the more common COPD where renal compensation has occurred typical blood gases are:

pH   7.30
Pa_{CO_2} 8.0 kPa (60 mmHg)
P_{O_2} 9.46 kPa (70 mmHg)
HCO_3 35 mmol l^{-1}

Treatment is aimed at the underlying cause for example improving ventilation using intermittent positive pressure ventilation if necessary. Alkali therapy has no place in chronic respiratory acidosis. In COPD the aim should be a H ion activity less than 56 nmol l^{-1} (pH> 7.25) rather than a normal Pa_{CO_2}. It is the acidity of the blood which is important and this will have been modified by renal compensatory HCO_3 retention. Repeated blood gas monitoring is of course mandatory. If intermittent positive pressure ventilation is used to produce a normal Pa_{CO_2} the patient will be left with a raised HCO_3 and metabolic alkalosis.

Respiratory alkalosis

$$pH = pK + \log \frac{HCO_3^-}{H_2CO_3} \qquad (1)$$

In this situation Pa_{CO_2} is reduced so that $\log \dfrac{HCO_3^-}{H_2CO_3}$ is increased with an increase in pH.

Causes of respiratory alkalosis

1 Hysterical hyperventilation.
2 Excessive intermittent hyperventilation.
3 Central nervous system disorder:
   head injury
   encephalitis.
4 Tissue hypoxia, for example; anaemia, gram negative sepsis.
5 Interstitial pulmonary disease.
6 Pulmonary oedema.
7 Hepatic failure.

Compensatory changes occur if the disturbance is prolonged. The kidney excretes more HCO_3 to restore pH to normal by reducing $\log \dfrac{HCO_3^-}{H_2CO_3}$

Again, treatment is that of the underlying cause.

In chronic alkalosis a rise in 2,3 DPG concentration prevents the increase in oxygen affinity which would occur due to a shift to the left of the oxygen dissociation curve because of the increase in pH.

Despite these apparent clear cut disturbances of acid base in practice there is often a mixed disorder. When confronted with an estimation of blood gases as with a plasma urea and electrolyte result it is important to isolate the most abnormal parameter since other abnormalities are possibly secondary to this or of a compensatory nature. In these circumstances an acid base diagram may be very helpful.

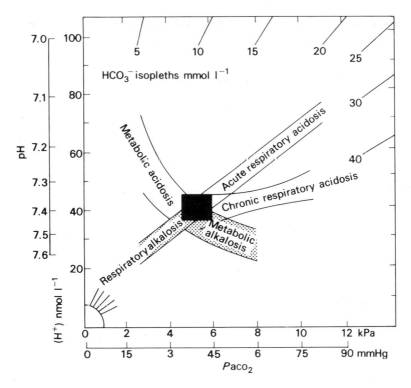

Fig. 13.5 Flenley acid base diagram.

The Flenley acid base diagram (Fig. 13.5) is an alternative way of looking at acid base disturbances and is in fact a modification of the Sigaard Anderson nomogram in which the bicarbonate buffer system only is considered. The linear relationship between H ion activity and $PaCO_2$ is plotted on a graph in which isopleths of equal HCO_3 concentration radiate out as a fan from the origin. 95% confidence limits are shown on the diagram. Serial values of blood gases are plotted to define the nature of the disturbance and its progress.

On the acid base diagram a point to the left of the normal pH of 7.4 implies an acidosis and a point on the right an alkalosis. The plasma bicarbonate can be read directly. The diagram is of great value during therapy to monitor the changes in response to treatment.

Anion gap

For electrical neutrality to exist the number of anions (negatively charged ions such as chloride and bicarbonate) must be equal to the number of cations (positively charged ions such as sodium and magnesium). The anion gap may be calculated in several different ways and the 'normal' range will therefore vary between laboratories. One method of calculation which can be done on a routine urea and electrolyte result is $(Na + K) - (Cl + HCO_3)$. This gives a value between 11–19 mmol l^{-1}. This value represents approximately the sum of the unmeasured anions which are protein, phosphate, lactate and 3 hydroxybutyrate.

Some laboratories exclude K in calculation of the anion gap which gives a lower normal range

Causes of an increased anion gap

1 Uraemic acidosis.
2 Ketoacidosis.
3 Salicylate poisoning.
4 Lactic acidosis.
5 Methanol, ethylene glycol and paraldehyde toxicity.

All of these causes are situations of acidosis but there are many other causes of acidosis in which the anion gap is not abnormal because chloride replaces bicarbonate, for example in diarrhoea.
6 Dehydration.
7 Therapy with sodium salts of strong acids where the acid anion is only slowly metabolised, for example sodium lactate. Antibiotics such as carbenicillin are administered as the sodium salt and the carbenicillin anion increases the anion gap.

Causes of low anion gap

1 Dilutional states.
2 Hypoalbuminaemia. Albumin at normal blood pH has a marked negative charge and therefore accounts for most of the anion gap.
3 Hypernatraemia, hypermagnesaemia, hypercalcaemia.
4 Paraproteinaemia. Here the increased viscosity of blood interferes with blood sampling.

5 Bromism. Some autoanalysers cannot distinguish between chloride and bromide so that an increase in bromide will present as a fall in the anion gap.

Minor variations in the anion gap should be interpreted with care since it is calculated from four variables. However it is of value in detecting an abnormality before more specific investigation can be undertaken. Therefore the practice of discontinuing chloride measurement in routine U and E results is to be deprecated.

ASSESSMENT OF BLOOD GAS MEASUREMENTS

Study the following blood gas measurements and assess which respiratory or metabolic disorder of acid base status the information suggests. Answers are given at the foot of the page.

1 pH   7.27
  $Paco_2$ 8.5 kPa (64 mmHg)
  HCO_3 37 mmol l^{-1}
  Pao_2 8.5 kPa (64 mmHg)
2 pH   7.50
  $Paco_2$ 6 kPa (45 mmHg)
  HCO_3 40 mmol l^{-1}
  Pao_2 11 kPa (8.3 mmHg)
3 pH   7.55
  $Paco_2$ 2.7 kPa (20 mmHg)
  HCO_3 22 mmol l^{-1}
  Pao_2 12 kPa (90 mmHg)
4 pH   7.31
  $Paco_2$ 4.0 kPa (30 mmHg)
  HCO_3 16 mmol l^{-1}
  Pao_2 13 kPa (98 mmHg)

(1) Respiratory acidosis. (2) Metabolic alkalosis. (3) Respiratory alkalosis. (4) Metabolic acidosis.

Chapter 14
Fluid Balance in Special Circumstances

CONGESTIVE CARDIAC FAILURE

Congestive cardiac failure (CCF) may be defined as circulatory insufficiency in which the heart fails to supply the metabolic needs of the body. There is a fall in cardiac output without a reduction in venous return. Organ perfusion is reduced and renal handling of Na and water is inappropriate. There is an increase in plasma volume, ECF volume and ICF volume.

Mechanisms involved in salt and water retention in congestive cardiac failure

1 The reduction in cardiac output reduced GFR and tubular reabsorption of Na and water are increased. The effective fall in circulating blood volume will increase aldosterone and ADH. The Na and water retention increase the filling pressure of the already impaired myocardium with further failure. The increased Na retention stimulates ADH secretion via the osmoreceptors.
2 The myocardial failure per se increases venous pressure which increases capillary hydrostatic pressure. This impairs return of fluid into the capillary with development of oedema.

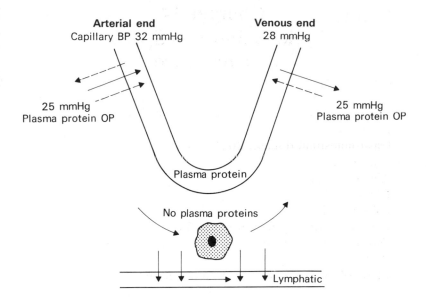

Fig. 14.1   Capillary circulation in congestive cardiac failure. (See Fig. 1.7, p. 14.)

Urine volume is reduced with an increase in specific gravity and osmolality unless diuretics are administered or there is intrinsic renal disease. CVP and pulmonary capillary wedge pressure are raised. Arterial Pao_2 falls. The acid base status is usually normal but haematocrit and plasma protein levels are reduced by a dilutional effect.

Treatment

Treatment includes use of diuretics and digitalis. Sodium and water restriction may be appropriate. In addition nitrates may be used to reduce the preload or nitroprusside to reduce the afterload on the heart.

Hypertension

There are many causes of hypertension some of which also cause electrolyte disturbances. These include the following:

Renal disease.
Endocrine disorders:
  Cushing's syndrome
  phaeochromocytoma
  pregnancy.
Vascular disease — coarctation of the aorta.
Essential hypertension.
Porphyria.
Acutely increased intracranial pressure.
Lead poisoning.

The electrolyte disturbances are those of the underlying cause but briefly:

1 Hyponatraemia may occur in hypertension treated by diuretic therapy, in renal disease and in accelerated hypertension with secondary hyperaldosteronism.
2 Hypernatraemia occurs in primary hyperaldosteronism.
3 Hypokalaemia occurs in diuretic therapy and increased aldosterone secretion.
4 Hypomagnesaemia occurs in primary hyperaldosteronism.
5 Metabolic alkalosis occurs with thiazide diuretics and in circumstances of excess concentration of aldosterone or corticosteroids. In these situations H and K are exchanged for sodium in the distal tubule with an increase in plasma HCO_3.
6 Total body water is increased in primary hyperaldosteronism and in hypertension with acromegaly. Total body water is reduced in renovascular hypertension.

RESPIRATORY DISEASE

Chronic obstructive pulmonary disease (COPD) associated with hypoxia may be accompanied by secondary polycythaemia and an increase in haematocrit. Plasma exchange in which the patients blood is removed and replaced with dextran or HPPF will improve blood flow, viscosity and oxygen delivery to the tissues.

When carbon dioxide (CO_2) retention occurs there is compensatory reabsorption of bicarbonate by the kidney in an attempt to maintain a normal pH.

Dyspnoea and hyperventilation are associated with increased water loss from the lungs and dehydration.

For the role of respiratory disease in acid base disturbance see Chapter 13.

GASTROINTESTINAL DISEASE

Pyloric obstruction

In this situation large volumes of gastric juice are vomited. Hydrogen, K, Na and Cl ions are lost with resulting falls in their plasma levels. Fluid loss results in reduction in circulating blood volume. Plasma bicarbonate (HCO_3) is raised and metabolic alkalosis occurs with tetany in extreme cases. Some respiratory depression occurs with retention of CO_2 so that carbonic acid levels rise in an attempt to restore pH to normal. The deficit of K reduces its exchange with sodium and H in the renal tubule so that aciduria may occur. In addition K enters cells in exchange for H. Later starvation with a decreased intake of carbohydrate and protein lead to catabolism with ketosis and an increase in blood urea.

Treatment consists of 0.9% sodium chloride with added KCl. Surgery is the definitive treatment for this condition.

Malabsorption

This presents a clinical combination of starvation and dehydration. Hyponatraemia and hypokalaemia occur with a reduction in circulating and intracellular fluid volumes.

Biliary and pancreatic fistulae

Up to 1 litre day^{-1} of alkaline fluid may be lost. This fluid will have a high Na and HCO_3 content. Metabolic acidosis occurs with a fall in plasma HCO_3, pH and P_{CO_2} and an increase in Cl to maintain anion balance. Hydrogen concentration is increased and if the situation is prolonged K levels fall.

Diarrhoea

Loss of water may amount to 10 litres daily in severe cases. Na loss may reach 350 mmol daily and K 45 mmol daily. Intestinal juice contains more HCO_3 than Cl so that plasma HCO_3 is more reduced than Cl and metabolic acidosis occurs. Lack of carbohydrate ingestion will lead to ketonaemia. Circulating blood volume will be reduced and if this is severe renal perfusion will be reduced with oliguria. Exudative diarrhoea will also result in increased protein loss.

Treatment

Fluid loss should be replaced with a solution containing

0.45% saline $+$ 40 mmol l^{-1} K and 45 mmol l^{-1} HCO_3.

In infants a different formula is used since losses of Na, K and Cl are likely to be less. Mention has already been made of oral replacement solutions for infants with diarrhoea (UNICEF/WHO glucose electrolyte solution). This solution should be used with caution taking into account the particular needs of the locality and age of the patient (see Chapter 6).

Protein losing enteropathy

Villous adenoma, inflammatory gastrointestinal tract disease, collagen disease and sprue may be associated with daily loss of 40–50 g of protein. This situation leads to a reduction in circulating blood volume and secondary hyperaldosteronism. There will then be a low plasma K and alkalosis. All plasma proteins are low. Treatment is that of the underlying disease, for example, steroids for ulcerative colitis.

Intestinal obstruction

If this is high the losses will be mainly gastric. In lower intestinal obstruction the loss will be as in diarrhoea, but because of the obstructed bowel inflammation and congestion occur with loss of protein. Treatment consists of replacing the losses, and surgery.

Peritonitis

Sequestration of fluid and electrolytes occurs in the peritoneal cavity. This will be increased by the osmotic effect of exudation of protein. At first there is salt and water loss; later hypovolaemia, hypotension and oliguric renal failure occur.

In any of these situations if due consideration is not given to the nature of the fluid losses inappropriate or inadequate therapy may be given. The electrolyte concentration of secretions is shown in Table A.4.

LIVER DISEASE

Acute liver failure

Hyperventilation with respiratory alkalosis occurs but it is unwise to correct this as deterioration in the patients condition may occur. Hypoxia is common and is due to a combination of factors:

1 Central nervous system depression.
2 Pulmonary oedema.
3 Infection.
4 Intrapulmonary shunting.

Hyponatraemia and hypokalaemia occur in 50% of patients at some time during the illness. This is partly dilutional. There is marked renal impairment of free water excretion. Hyponatraemia also occurs due to loss of sodium into the cell when the activity of Na/K ATPase is reduced. This is the sick cell syndrome (see Chapter 6).

Chronic liver disease

Fluid retention occurs resulting in oliguria, ascites and peripheral oedema. In cirrhosis some disturbance exists prior to the onset of ascites, in that there is a reduction in total body K with a normal or low plasma urea. Plasma volume and ECF volume are increased with an increase in exchangeable sodium.

As ascites develops plasma protein levels fall especially plasma albumin resulting in a reduction in effective plasma volume and renal plasma flow. This increases activity of the renin angiotensin system with secondary hyperaldosteronism. Aldosterone increases reabsorption of sodium from the distal tubule in exchange for H and K. Therefore there is a temporary increase in plasma Na with reduced K and H and a mild metabolic alkalosis. Water is retained with Na. Cirrhosis results in increased splanchnic capillary pressure which in conjunction with the overloading of lymphatic reabsorption and reduced plasma colloid osmotic pressure results in ascites. Although the effective plasma volume is reduced the actual volume is increased. Some of this is within distended portal veins. Usually the raised plasma ammonia stimulates the respiratory centre and hyperventilation occurs.

Causes of alkalosis in cirrhosis

1 Hypokalaemic alkalosis associated with intracellular acidosis.
2 The respiratory centre stimulation due to hyperammonaemia and hypoxia.
3 Renal excretion of H due to the secondary hyperaldosteronism.

Blood urea is low owing to reduced synthesis by the liver. Urine is often hyperosmolar compared to plasma because the kidney is unable to excrete a dilute urine.

At a later stage of liver failure renal failure occurs. This is the hepatorenal syndrome. The most likely cause of this is endotoxin production. It seems unlikely that the reduction in effective plasma volume is important in pathogenesis of the renal failure in cirrhosis. GFR and renal blood flow may fall rapidly with an increase in plasma renin activity.

Management

1 Diuretics. Potent loop diuretics such as frusemide induce further hypokalaemia and alkalosis and should therefore be avoided. They may precipitate hepatic encephalopathy and do nothing to improve renal perfusion. Both thiazides and frusemide produce hyperuricaemia but bumetanide may have an advantage by producing less urate retention.

Hyperaldosteronism is improved by spironolactone. This will conserve K but results in relatively poor excretion of sodium.

Triamterene and amiloride are diuretics which conserve K but there may be progressive resistance to their action if they are used alone.
2 Dietary sodium should be restricted.
3 Paracentesis should only be used to relieve cardiorespiratory

distress as it removes a large amount of protein, with a risk of infection. The net result is a further reduction in plasma volume, increase in aldosterone and ADH production.

4 Steroids have been recommended by some workers to increase free water and sodium excretion.

5 Salt poor albumin may be used in an attempt to raise plasma albumin.

ALCOHOLISM

Alcohol is a diuretic which increases free water clearance by inhibition of ADH. This is associated with a mild metabolic acidosis. As Na, K and Cl retention occur with an increase in osmolality production of ADH is stimulated and an antidiuretic phase then occurs.

Chronic alcoholics have a reduced plasma K. Body sodium is usually increased. It is well recognised that chronic alcoholic beer drinkers may suffer severe hyponatraemia and hypoosmolality (see Chapter 6).

Malnutrition, vomiting and diarrhoea are common in alcoholics and will have their effects on electrolyte balance. Deficiency of calcium and magnesium occur due to increased renal excretion, malnutrition and increased intestinal loss.

In the normal population ethanol is known to induce hypoglycaemia. In a recent study infusion of ethanol was shown to produce the following changes:

1 Hypoglycaemia due to inhibition of hepatic gluconeogenesis.

2 An increase in blood lactate, hydroxybutyrate and free fatty acids.

3 Reduced growth hormone concentration.

4 Raised plasma cortisol concentration.

Clearly the inclusion of alcohol in regimes for parenteral nutrition may have serious side effects.

DIABETES

The water, electrolyte and acid base abnormalities in diabetes are due to absolute or relative lack of insulin causing impairment of glucose utilisation and gluconeogenesis. In the absence of insulin glucose uptake into cells is very slow and therefore plasma glucose rises, increasing the effective osmotic pressure of ECF with passage of water from cells to maintain isotonicity.

As blood glucose rises the renal threshold for glucose is reached (10 mmol l^{-1}). Glucose then appears in the urine and the osmotic diuresis prevents the reabsorption of water Na, K and Cl. This state of affairs may continue until considerable dehydration reduces GFR and oliguria occurs despite hyperglycaemia. As dehydration progresses less Na reaches the distal tubule and hence less is available for exchange with K and H and their retention is a significant cause of metabolic acidosis.

The resultant effects of this are to produce progressive cellular dehydration and loss of water together with Na, K and Cl into urine. In uncontrolled hyperglycaemia therefore total body osmolality is raised but plasma sodium and chloride are normal or low because of the dilutional effects of water from cells. If however a raised plasma sodium is found this indicates *severe* water loss (hyperglycaemic hyperosmolar non-ketotic diabetic coma). Direct measurements of plasma osmolality are very helpful and can be used to estimate the water deficit (see Chapter 5). Hyperglycaemia as already discussed is a less potent stimulus for ADH production than hypernatraemia for the same level of osmolality.

In evaluating plasma electrolytes to assess deficits it is essential to ensure that there is no serious hyperlipidaemia producing pseudohyponatraemia which leads to gross underestimation of the extent of the dehydration (see Chapter 6, p. 113).

Since normal carbohydrate utilisation is impaired in diabetes large amounts of fat are metabolised resulting in increased ketone body production. When these organic acids are added to ECF they are initially buffered producing a fall in plasma bicarbonate. Hyperventilation occurs with a fall in plasma Pa_{CO_2} in an attempt to compensate for the impending metabolic acidosis. Eventually these compensatory mechanisms become exhausted and pH falls (see Chapter 13).

Water loss is in excess of electrolyte loss and glucose is less effective than other solutes in stimulating thirst. *Hypertonic* dehydration occurs and the patient cannot take sufficient fluids orally because of vomiting, anorexia and impending coma. As the water loss can be extreme a reduction in circulating blood volume,

Table 14.1   Fluids lost in diabetic ketosis.

	Osmolality	Sodium concentration
Skin, lungs (water	0	0
Kidney	Iso or hypertonic	25–100 mmol l^{-1}
Vomit	Isotonic	50–80 mmol l^{-1}

hypotension and shock eventually occur. Abdominal pain may be due to ketosis per se although it is often misdiagnosed as a surgical emergency. A marked leucocytosis may occur. Acute pancreatitis may be precipitated. In diabetic coma mortality may be as high as 10% but recent advances in management may reduce this.

Glucose concentrations can be measured by enzymatic means using glucose oxidase or dehydrogenase. Some drugs interfere with such estimations. Portable machines such as the Reflomat reflectance meter utilise glucose oxidase impregnated strips and can be used for repeated capillary blood sugar measurements.

Management of uncontrolled diabetes

Insulin.
Fluid replacement.

The relative amounts of insulin and fluid required depend to some extent on whether diabetic ketoacidosis or hyperosmolar hyperglycaemic non-ketotic coma is present.

Diabetic ketoacidosis

This may be due to a precipitating cause in a stable diabetic, for example, chest infection, myocardial infarction or may occur at presentation in a young diabetic. The diagnosis may be suspected from air hunger (Kussmaul's respiration) and the smell of ketones on the breath and confirmed by urine and blood sugar measurement. Too many patients develop ketoacidosis because of delay in diagnosis or poor management of the diabetic state during intercurrent illness.

INVESTIGATIONS

Blood glucose.
Urea and electrolytes.
Haemoglobin and haematocrit.
Arterial blood gases.
Blood culture.

These are urgent investigations which should be carried out in the casualty department.

INTRAVENOUS INFUSION

A large bore cannula sited peripherally is essential. In addition CVP measurement is valuable especially in the elderly in whom large volumes of fluid replacement may result in cardiac failure. One litre of 0.9% saline may be given over 30 minutes whilst results are awaited. 20 units of soluble insulin or the less antigenic neutral or Actrapid insulin for a newly diagnosed patient may be added to the infusion with good mixing. Thereafter 1 litre 0.9% saline may be given hourly or under CVP control. If the patient remains hypotensive with a low CVP after several litres of saline then consider giving human plasma protein fraction to increase colloid osmotic pressure.

INSULIN

Increasing use is being made of continuous intravenous insulin infusion with the aim of producing an effective plasma insulin level between 20–200 μ units ml^{-1}. Smaller doses of insulin used in this way are effective (2.4–12 units hourly). This has advantages over subcutaneous injection which is too erratic and over intermittent boluses of intravenous insulin. With these small doses given continuously i.v. blood glucose falls at the same rate as with larger doses of insulin. Hypokalaemia and cerebral oedema are less likely, the increase in blood lactate is reduced and late hypoglycaemia is also less common. Insulin dose will fall dramatically as acidosis improves (0.5–2 units hourly). One method uses a continuous infusion pump to give 6 units soluble insulin hour^{-1}. If the response is unsatisfactory the dose of insulin is doubled, and when blood glucose reaches 10 mmol l^{-1} the dose is reduced. It is very rare to need more than 30 units hour^{-1} unless steroids or sympathomimetics are in use.

Usually blood sugar falls at a rate of about 5 mmol hour^{-1}. When it has reached 10 mmol l^{-1}, 6 g glucose hour^{-1} should be added to the infusion. Some workers add albumin or haemaccel to the insulin infusion to reduce absorption of insulin to the plastic of the administration system. However with high concentrations of insulin this is not necessary.

POTASSIUM

As glucose begins to enter the cells under the influence of insulin it is accompanied by K so that plasma K concentration falls and supplements will be required to prevent dangerous hypokalaemia. About 20 mmol K may be given after the first or second litre in each litre 0.9% saline. Some authorities prefer to give K only when plasma K is 4.5 mmol or less when 13–26 mmol hourly are infused. The total dose required may be 50–250 mmol especially if bicarbonate is used. It is mandatory to measure plasma K and glucose hourly to modify subsequent K and insulin dosage and to measure urine ketones and glucose. Less frequent blood gas measurement allows correction of pH.

BICARBONATE

The pH will correct itself over 5–6 hours (after 6–7 litres saline) but if the pH is very low, for example less than 7.1 and has not improved over 2 hours, then $NaHCO_3$ should be used (1.4% $NaHCO_3$, which contains 1 mmol in each 6 ml. 50 ml may be given or 100 ml if the pH is less than 7.0). The danger of this is that a left shift of the O_2 dissociation curve occurs with impaired release of O_2 in the tissues. The low pH in diabetic ketoacidosis results in a low 2,3 DPG which balances the effect of acidosis on the O_2 dissociation curve so that tissue oxygenation is normal. If bicarbonate is transfused rapidly to correct pH, the low 2,3 DPG will be unopposed and the O_2 dissociation curve shift to the left with a rapid fall in tissue oxygenation. 2,3 DPG levels may take several days to return to normal because phosphate is being rapidly taken up by the cells. Therefore bicarbonate should be used with great care and phosphate added to the i.v. regime.

As conscious level improves oral fluid may be given. When the patient is eating, intravenous insulin may be discontinued and subsutaneous insulin give b.d. or t.d.s. The intravenous infusion should be continued for about 48 hours. If the blood glucose fall is dramatic then 5% dextrose may be substituted but with small doses of intravenous insulin this is rarely necessary if the patient is allowed to eat as soon as he is able.

Urine and plasma osmolality are a valuable guide to treatment.

Hyperosmolar hyperglycaemic non-ketotic coma

Hyperosmolar hyperglycaemic non-ketotic coma now forms 10–20% of causes of diabetic coma. This tends to occur in the elderly and usually the hyperglycaemia has been present for weeks before admission but there are no ketones in the urine. Blood glucose can become very high (greater than 40 mmol l^{-1}) and hypertonicity severe (plasma osmolality > 350 mosmol kg^{-1}). Plasma Na may be greater than 155 mmol^{-1}. Hyperthermia, seizures and focal central nervous system signs may occur in addition to impaired conscious level. The mortality in a recent series was 44% and was related to age above 60, uraemia, hyperosmolality but not to the degree or rate of fall of hyperglycaemia.

MANAGEMENT

1 0.45% saline can be alternated with 0.9% saline. Although plasma Na is high loss of water and Na is very marked and it is essential to replace some of the Na deficit. These patients have a greater fluid deficit than ketotic patients because of the longer history but as this occurs in older patients with an increased incidence of heart disease, renal impairment, rapid fluid replacement is fraught with danger. Pulmonary oedema and disequilibration may occur.

A CVP line is essential in management although it does not reflect preload on the left heart. Needs should be tailored to the specific patient and hypovolaemia corrected fairly urgently.

The alternating regime is probably safe unless plasma sodium is greater than 155 mmol l^{-1} since plasma glucose should be falling and plasma osmolality due to hyperglycaemia will also be falling and therefore some increase in plasma Na may act as a buffer to prevent too rapid a fall in osmolality which would precipitate cerebral oedema due to increased intracerebral water. Some workers prefer isotonic saline with its increased risk of Na overload relying on careful fluid balance, CVP and slower correction, because of the danger of hypotonic saline producing fatal cerebral oedema. The total Na deficit is likely to be about 400 mmol and water deficits are very variable (5–20 litres).

2 Less insulin will be required. 24 hour insulin requirements rarely exceed 50 units. In this situation as glucose is taken up into the cell accompanied by water, intracellular volume increases at the expense of ECF. Following rehydration endogenous production of insulin may be adequate.

3 As has already been seen idiogenic osmoles are formed in the brain in situations of acute dehydration and this may be facilitated by insulin. Then isotonic water intoxication may be precipitated during fluid replacement therapy.

Potassium loss may have been extreme (5–10 mmol kg^{-1} body weight) and requires slow replacement. The risk of a precipitous, dangerous fall in K is greater in the absence of acidosis. It may be unwise to give insulin until plasma K is known to be greater than 4.0 mmol l^{-1}. K should be added to the infusion from the onset of treatment. 25–50 mmol may be required hourly. Oral K should be continued after the acute episode for one week because the total body K deficit may be as much as 400–1000 mmol.

If diabetic coma of any sort is present a nasogastric tube should be inserted to keep the stomach as empty as possible. A urinary catheter is useful but may lead to infection.

Subcutaneous heparin should be used as prophaxis against deep vein thrombosis if the blood glucose levels are particularly high.

ECG monitoring is valuable to assess K status. Diagnosis and treatment of any underlying cause is extremely important. A search should be made for infection and the relevant specimens taken before starting the appropriate antibiotic.

The WBC count is raised in ketoacidosis without infection.

Lactic acidosis

This may be precipitated by phenformin. There is inhibition of oxidative phosphorylation and an increase in anaerobic glycolysis. The situation is worsened by renal insufficiency. There is a high mortality, large amounts of bicarbonate may be required for treatment. If ketosis is not marked but pH is low the anion gap will be raised (see Chapter 13).

Other circumstances in which blood sugar is raised include severe stress, burns, after subarachnoid haemorrhage, septicaemia and total parenteral nutrition (see Chapter 12).

DIABETICS REQUIRING SURGERY

This is one of the most important practical problems for housemen today. The precise management will be dependent on the extent of the surgery and whether it is elective or emergency but guidelines may be given.

Biguanides predispose to lactic acidosis and should be *stopped*.

Sulphonylureas. Long acting ones such as chlorpropamide should be stopped at least 3 days before operation and a change made to a short acting one such as glibenclamide for minor surgery or to soluble insulin for anything more extensive.

Insulin dependent diabetics

A continuous infusion of glucose and insulin should be set up 30 minutes preoperatively to give 2 units of insulin, 10 g glucose and 2 mmol K per hour. This may be continued until the patient is eating. Blood glucose and K levels need monitoring, Many factors influence requirements, for example, the stress response to trauma, the extent of preoperative starvation and adequacy of control of diabetes preoperatively.

Administration of Hartmann's solution to diabetics intra-operatively is associated with a significant rise in plasma glucose compared to non diabetics or alternative fluid administration. This is probably due to the lactate content (29 mmol l^{-1}). Lactate is an important gluconeogenic precursor especially in starved catabolic patients and may in part account for the increase in blood sugar. Saline is not contraindicated. Blood transfusion increases insulin requirement because although the glucose content of blood is low lactate and pyruvate are high and these stimulate glyconeogenesis especially in diabetics. In the long term Mg and PO_4 replacement should be kept in mind.

In diabetic patients glucose induced hyperkalaemia is not uncommon and may be due in part to hypoaldosteronism and hyporeninism. Aldosterone is important in protecting against hyperkalaemia but not all diabetics with low aldosterone have glucose induced hyperkalaemia.

POISONING

The most important aspect of treatment of drug overdose is early resuscitation and supportive care. Most drugs are metabolised in the liver and excreted in the urine. Drugs which are non protein bound are excreted by passive glomerular filtration. Rarely passive tubular diffusion also occurs.

Early excessive therapeutic zeal should be guarded against. For example gastric lavage is positively dangerous in corrosive poisoning, may cause water intoxication and increase absorption of the poison. Following initial resuscitation, measures to increase excretion of certain drugs may be appropriate. These measures include:

1 Forced diuresis.
2 Peritoneal dialysis.
3 Haemodialysis.
4 Haemoperfusion.

Forced diuresis

Most drugs are weak acids or bases which at the pH of the body exist partly as undissociated molecules. Drugs which are weak acids will ionise to a greater extent in alkaline solution. Cell membranes are more permeable to drugs which are lipid soluble and non-ionised. Therefore when a drug is ionised it fails to diffuse back into the circulation from the renal tubule and more will be excreted. Changing the pH of the urine to alter the degree of ionisation therefore will effect the excretion of the drug. Only drugs which are excreted in the active form by the kidney will be affected. For acidic drugs the ionisation will be increased in an alkaline urine and for basic drugs ionisation is increased in an acid urine.

Forced diuresis will *only* be effective in the following circumstances:

1 When most of the drug is excreted in the toxic, unchanged form, in other words, the drug is not metabolised.
2 The drug is distributed mainly in the ECF.

3 The drug is minimally protein bound.
4 The drug must be non-ionised at pH 7 but ionised at pH 8 (acidic drugs) or pH 6 (basic drugs).

The technique of forced diuresis involves transfusion of large amounts of fluid together with administration of a diurectic.

CONTRAINDICATIONS TO FORCED DIURESIS

1 Shock.
2 Impaired renal function.
3 Heart failure.
4 The elderly.

PROCEDURE FOR FORCED DIURESIS

Set up i.v. line taking blood for
  U & E
  sugar
  drug levels.

CVP line
Urinary catheter — measure urine pH
Arterial blood pH

Forced alkaline diuresis

This is indicated for acidic drugs:

1 Phenobarbitone (plasma level > 100 mg l^{-1}).
2 Barbitone (plasma level > 100 mg l^{-1}).
3 Salicylates (plasma level > 500 mg l^{-1} or in a child 300 mg l^{-1}).
4 Lithium.

FORCED ALKALINE DIURESIS

1 Frusemide 20 mg i.v.
2 In first hour:
  500 ml 5% dextrose
  500 ml 1.4% $NaHCO_3$
  500 ml 5% dextrose.
3 If urine flow then less than 3 ml min^{-1} discontinue diuresis.

4 If urine flow more than 3 ml min^{-1} continue to maintain urine flow 500 ml hour^{-1}, giving boluses of frusemide 20 mg as required.
5 Add 10–20 mmol K to each litre of fluid.
6 Maintain urine pH 7.5–8.5 by adjusting amount of NaHCO$_3$ in infusion.

Forced acid diuresis

This is indicated for weak bases which are normally partially ionised in solution.

1 Quinine.
2 Amphetamine.
3 Fenfluramine.
4 Monoamine oxidase inhibitors.
5 Phencyclidine.

FORCED ACID DIURESIS

1 Frusemide 20 mg.
2 In first hour
1000 ml 5% dextrose.
+ 500 ml 0.9% NaCl.
+ 10 g arginine (or lysine) hydrochloride.
Intravenously over 30 minutes.
3 If urine flow then less than 3 ml min^{-1}, discontinue diuresis.
4 If urine flow more than 3 ml min^{-1} continue to maintain urine flow 500 ml hour^{-1}, giving boluses of frusemide 20 mg i.v. as reguired.
5 Add 10–20 mmol K to each litre of fluid.
6 Maintain urine pH 5.5–6.5 with oral NH$_4$Cl 4g 2 hourly.

During forced diuresis measure:

Urine pH hourly.
Plasma and urine elecxtrolytes 4 hourly.
Keep accurate fluid balance chart.

COMPLICATIONS

Forced diuresis requires the patient to be in an intensive care unit as very great care should be exercised with this technique. In spite of this complications include:

1 Water intoxication.
2 Cerebral oedema.
3 Electrolyte and acid base disturbance.

Peritoneal dialysis

This technique has even less application in the treatment of drug overdose although it has been used for poisoning with lithium and ethylene glycol.

Haemodialysis

This technique is the treatment of choice for severe poisoning with lithium, methyl and ethyl alcohol. Very rarely it may be useful in removing phenobarbitone, barbitone and salicylates if the patient's renal function is impaired so that forced alkaline diuresis is contra-indicated.

Haemoperfusion

This technique involves passing the patients blood over an adsorbent such as charcoal or a resin which has been coated with a substance such as cellulose to prevent platelet and fibrinogen consumption.

Indications for haemoperfusion

1 The drug should be readily taken up onto the adsorbent.
2 Much of the drug should be in equilibrium with plasma water.
3 The blood level of the drug should be directly related to its toxic effects.
4 The technique must significantly improve on the body's normal mechanisms of elimination of the drug.

If the drug is non toxic or has a large volume of distribution, is irreversible in its action or has an antidote then haemoperfusion is contraindicated.

Heparinisation will be required which may lead to haemorrhage.

In addition loss of platelets, white blood cells and clotting factors are recognised complications. The plasma concentrations of calcium, glucose, urea, creatinine and urate fall.

Details of abnormalities to be found in specific drug overdose are beyond the scope of the book but relevant characteristic features do occur in salicylate overdose.

Salicylate overdose

1 Stimulation of the respiratory centre causes hyperventilation with a fall in Pa_{CO_2}, and an increase in pH. Renal compensation reduces reabsorption of HCO_3 producing a fall in plasma HCO_3.

2 Later metabolic acidosis develops with ketonaemia.

CENTRAL NERVOUS SYSTEM DISEASE

In the brain the cerebrospinal fluid (CSF) is in very close association with ECF. If K, Mg or Ca is infused intravenously into animals there is little change in cisternal CSF concentration of the ions infused. Therefore entry of these ions into cerebral ECF is slow at least and powerful mechanisms in the blood brain barrier (BBB) and choroid plexus exist which keep the cerebral ionic content constant. Water is however freely permeable between brain and systemic ECF and therefore changes in plasma osmolality are rapidly transmitted to the central nervous system. In hypernatraemia where water is lost from the cells the brain is able to create idiogenic osmoles which 'hold' water within the brain.

The BBB and blood CSF barriers are freely permeable to CO_2 but much less permeable to HCO_3 and cerebral ECF has a relatively low buffering capacity. Brain pH is very stable. Small changes in brain stem CO_2 alter ventilation to restore pH to normal. Although the BBB actively transports HCO_3, changes in the concentration of this ion occur slowly within the brain.

Abnormal osmolality and the brain

Hypernatraemia associated with hyperosmolality is usually due to water deficiency and caused by an impaired conscious level with reduced voluntary intake in response to thirst. Hypernatraemia may cause physical damage to the brain. Since the brain is situated within the closed cranium sudden expansion or contraction of one compartment will effect the other compartments. Administration of mannitol may produce such fluid shifts that in infants a subdural haematoma due to tearing of the delicate veins occurs as the cerebral substance shrinks.

If dehydration is corrected too rapidly further osmotic swelling may occur within brain cells. In this context administration of 5% dextrose is akin to giving water.

Water intoxication producing osmotic swelling of the brain is distinct from cerebral oedema due to trauma, neoplasm or infection when there is an increase in Na and loss of K as well as increased water. Hyponatraemia does not seem to be associated with such a risk of permanent brain damage as hypernatraemia. Rapid reduction in blood urea during dialysis may produce cerebral symptoms of water intoxication because exchange of urea across the BBB is slow and therefore the brain will be hypertonic in relation to the rest of the body and as such will take up water.

Causes of hyponatraemia of cerebral origin

1 Meningitis especially tuberculous.
2 Severe head injury.
3 Cerebral tumour.
4 Subarachnoid haemorrhage.
5 Hypertensive encephalopathy.
6 Encephalitis.
7 Poliomyelitis.
8 Cerebral abscess.
9 Guillain Barré syndrome.
10 Acute intermittent porphyria.

These situations are due mainly to high circulating ADH hormone levels (see Chapter 5). Treatment is that of the underlying cause and water restriction.

Management of cerebral oedema

Management of cerebral oedema hinges on the following:

1 Maintenance of good oxygenation.

2 Hyperventilation to reduce cerebral blood flow.

3 CSF drainage. It is mandatory to remember that ill advised lumbar puncture in the presence of raised intracranial pressure may precipitate coning with fatal consequences. CSF drainage should therefore be effected from the ventricular system in these circumstances.

4 Hypertonic solutions. Mannitol exerts a profound osmotic diuretic effect and reduces brain volume.

5 Frusemide in addition to its effect as a loop diuretic also reduces the rate of CSF production.

DISORDERS DUE TO HEAT

Heat exhaustion

This occurs when insufficient water is taken to replace the losses due to sweating. Normally excessive thirst will lead to an increased voluntary water intake. However, if water is not available or the patient has an impaired conscious level then heat exhaustion is likely. Marked hypernatraemia and hyperosmolality occur. Treatment consists of 5% dextrose intravenously or if the diagnosis is not clear and salt loss may have occurred then 0.9% saline is suitable.

Heat exhaustion due to salt depletion occurs when salt is inadequately replaced during long term sweating. Fatigue and anorexia occur with vomiting and circulatory collapse. The salt content of sweat is about 45 mmol l^{-1} in these circumstances and the deficit may be calculated (see Chapter 6). This situation develops over a period of weeks. Treatment consists of giving salt to unacclimatised patients.

Anhidrotic heat exhaustion occurs after several months residence in a hot climate. Defective sweating occurs with an increase in body temperature. Potassium depletion may be important in the aetiology in which case supplements should be given. When heat stroke occurs the best treatment is cooling by evaporative heat loss from warm skin hence it is important to maintain peripheral vasodilation.

Malignant hyperthermia

This syndrome consists of a rapid rise in temperature (in excess of 2°C hour^{-1}) with rigidity and cyanosis precipitated by exposure to some anaesthetic agents in particular the combination of sux-amethonium and halothane. Early changes which occur are a fall in pH, a rise in Pa_{CO_2} and K.

BURNS

The essential problem in burns is the rapid fluid loss from the circulation. Up to 50% of the circulating blood volume may be lost in the first 6 hours and as the loss is diffuse and difficult to recognise or assess it may be underestimated with subsequent dangerous delay in treatment.

The local lesion

The oedema fluid has much the same electrolyte content as plasma with a protein content of $40-50 \, g \, l^{-1}$. The protein in interstitial burn fluid comes from circulating plasma because of the increased permeability of the damaged capillaries. This reduces plasma protein osmotic pressure and increases interstitial fluid in the non-burned parts of the body. Much of the Na lost into interstitial fluid enters cells whereas K is lost into ECF and plasma. The increase in capillary permeability is maximal during the first 8 hours after the burn and gradually decreases over the next 36 hours. Hypoxia in the damaged area may increase anaerobic metabolism with metabolic acidosis and this will further impair tissue perfusion. Widespread damage to blood vessels causes thrombosis and red blood cell aggregation. For each 10% of the body surface burned there is a 7% reduction on red blood cells.

Because of the loss of intravascular protein there is a reduction in effective plasma volume. Further loss of fluid occurs due to the longer lasting persistent evaporation of water from the damaged skin surface. This loss varies with the temperature and humidity of the environment but can be 3 litres daily. Large heat losses will occur due to latent heat of vaporisation.

Systemic disturbances

Hypovolaemia may be severe enough to produce shock. There will be oliguria and a reduction in cardiac output which may be associated with the production of myocardial depressant factor. Catecholamine release increases peripheral resistance. The loss of plasma is in excess of the loss in red cell mass so that haematocrit rises. There is an increase in viscosity with sludging of red blood cells in the microcirculation. This produces further hypoxia and metabolic acidosis. Red blood cells may release large quantities of pigment which when deposited in the renal tubules will further impair renal function.

The metabolic response to trauma is activated. Hypercatabolism leads to increased K loss and subsequently if untreated to hypokalaemia. Rarely can sufficient calories be given either orally or parenterally to prevent breakdown of the patient's own muscle protein.

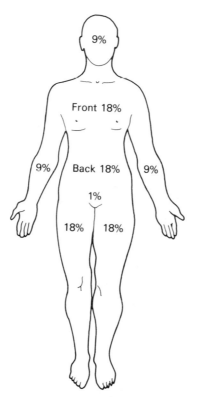

Fig. 14.2 Rule of nine for calculation of the percentage body surface area burned in an adult.

Inhalation damage may occur. Heat damage rarely extends beyond the trachea but inhalation of chemicals such as aldehydes may produce pneumonitis. Adult respiratory distress syndrome due to sepsis or oxygen toxicity may occur when pulmonary capillary permeability is markedly increased.

Gastrointestinal ulceration may occur as may paralytic ileus with all its attendant electrolyte problems.

Management

Many formulae exist for fluid replacement in burns. These should be used as a guide only. The first priority is *early fluid replacement*.

The intravenous infusion of fluid should start as soon as possible to prevent the fall in cardiac output and to maintain renal perfusion. If a patient with burns develops renal failure his changes of survival are considerably reduced.

Most formulae depend on replacement according to the percentage of skin burned.

Burns in small children do not conform to this rule exactly since the head and neck represents a greater proportion of the surface area in this age group.

One commonly used formula for all burns is as follows:

$$\frac{Body\ weight\ (kg)}{2} \times \%\ area\ burned = \text{ml of fluid required in first 4 hours.}$$

The work of Muir and Barclay divided the first 36 hours after a burn into periods of:

1 4 hours.
2 4 hours.
3 4 hours.
4 6 hours.
5 6 hours.
6 12 hours.

The expected fluid requirement in each of these periods is given by the formula. Most of the fluid requirements may be given as plasma but as we have already seen red cells are lost so that blood should be given as part of the fluid replacement. One formula for giving blood is to give 1% of the patients normal blood volume ($70-75$ ml kg^{-1}) for each percentage full thickness burn.

In an adult a burn of greater than 15% requires intravenous infusion but in a child this will be required with a burn of 10% surface area.

The clinical state of the patient is a good guide to management but additional monitoring is very important and the following are essential:

1 Urine output.
2 Urine osmolality, plasma osmolality.
3 Haemoglobin, haematocrit.
4 CVP.

Urine output depends not only on the renal perfusion and state of the circulation but also on the water retention that occurs when the metabolic response to trauma is activated. What is important is that the volume of urine excreted should be sufficient at whatever osmolar content to excrete the body's osmolar load. In conditions of stress and trauma with maximal ADH activity the concentration of urine is less than 1000 mosmol kg^{-1}. An average normal osmolar output of 1200 mosmoles therefore would require a urine volume of at least 1200 ml for its excretion or 50 ml hourly. If the urine output is low but osmolality high this indicates poor renal perfusion and is an indication to increase the rate of transfusion. A good urine volume alone however is of little value if its osmolality is low. This implies impaired renal function. In a severe burn hourly urine volume must be measured accurately and a urinary catheter is justified.

Maintenance of circulating blood volume and urine output therefore are the aims of fluid therapy. The use of blood and plasma have already been referred to. Other plasma expanders may also be used in limited volumes (see Chapter 10). The use of crystalloid solutions such as Hartmann's will often produce a good urine output but its effect on resuscitation as judged by the CVP is minimal. Measurement of the haematocrit is a useful indication of the plasma deficit in many circumstances but in burns it must be remembered that there is a variable loss of red blood cells and the significance of the haematocrit after transfusion of whole blood is difficult to determine.

The burned patient will have ongoing fluid losses and later considerable blood loss may occur during repeated surgery for desloughing. In an inhalation burn in which ARDS develops plasma transfused intravenously may appear in pulmonary aspirate. This situation is very difficult to treat. In addition to specific fluid replacement other factors deserve attention. The humidity of the environment should be increased along with the temperature in order to reduce water and heat loss and hence energy expenditure. Treatment of pain with generous doses of narcotic analgesics will reduce the stress response. Parenteral nutrition may be required to provide adequate energy and protein needs.

EFFECT OF DRUGS ON ELECTROLYTE BALANCE

Diuretics

Acetazolamide inhibits carbonic anhydrase activity in the proximal tubule thereby blocking exchange of H for Na there. Plasma H increases and pH falls and therefore this may be valuable in the treatment of metabolic alkalosis. Plasma HCO_3 and Na fall and hyperchloraemia occurs because Cl is reabsorbed in the ascending limb of the loop of Henle. Na is exchanged for K in the distal tubule resulting in hypokalaemia.

Thiazide diuretics selectively inhibit reabsorption of Na and Cl in the early distal tubule so that plasma Na and Cl fall. There is an increase in exchange of Na with K and H in the distal tubule so that hypokalaemia and metabolic alkalosis may occur with an increase in plasma HCO_3.

Frusemide and ethacrynic acid inhibit Na and Cl reabsorption in the ascending limb of the loop of Henle. Both are potent diuretics and produce a fall in plasma Na, Cl and plasma volume. There is exchange of Na with K and H in the distal tubule with a fall in plasma K and metabolic alkalosis. Differential diagnosis from dilutional hyponatraemia may be difficult but blood volume, CVP, plasma proteins and haematocrit may help to differentiate (see Chapter 6).

Spironolactone is an aldosterone antagonist acting on the distal tubule so that sodium is not reabsorbed in exchange for H and K and a small increase in plasma K and H occur with a small fall in plasma sodium.

Triamterene and amiloride act similarly although they are not aldosterone antagonists.

Mannitol is one of the osmotic diuretics.

Glucocorticoids

In primary and secondary adrenal insufficiency with lack of hydrocortisone, even with normal mineralocorticoid activity there is inability to excrete a water load and susceptibility to water intoxication. In primary hyperaldosteronism and Cushing's syndrome with increased cortisol production severe hypokalaemia may occur due to increased K loss in the urine. Raised cortisol levels are known to be associated with hypokalaemic alkalosis. Patients with Cushing's syndrome may have an expanded plasma volume and occasionally mild oedema. Usually plasma sodium is normal.

Many drugs may influence water and electrolyte composition of the body. For example carbenoxolone and liquorice derivatives give rise to sodium retention. Large doses of parenteral antibiotics may give a large sodium load. Certain electrolyte solutions for parenteral administration are incompatible with certain drugs; for example tetracyclines will precipitate in Hartmann's solution (because of its calcium content). Erythromycin should not be added to 5% dextrose solution. The activity of lignocaine and mexilitine (type I antiarrythmic drugs) is reduced in the presence of low ECF K.

The nature of parenteral fluids themselves is also important. Large volumes of 5% dextrose (pH 4.0) used as a vehicle for infusion of drugs for example may produce metabolic acidosis and large volumes of 8.4% sodium bicarbonate (1 mmol ml^{-1}) will provide a large salt load which is especially dangerous in congestive cardiac failure.

Chapter 15
Practicalities of Setting Up
Infusion Lines

About 20 million intravenous infusions (i.v.i.) are set up annually in the United Kingdom.

PERIPHERAL INFUSIONS

Insertion of a peripheral intravenous line is now commonplace in medical practice. It may be a life saving procedure in cases of hypovolaemic shock or more simply a means to supply adequate fluid therapy for the patient. In any event skilful insertion of a cannula with the minimum of complications should be the aim of all junior doctors.

Equipment

1 The infusion fluid should be checked by the doctor for the following points:
(a) Is the fluid clear?
(b) Is the fluid correct in type and concentration and does it correspond with the prescription chart?
2 The infusion fluid and administration set should be assembled aseptically and all air bubbles excluded from the system. The risk of air embolus is greatly increased in the presence of a congenital right to left intracardiac shunt.
3 Skin preparation. This does not totally prevent bacterial contamination. One of the alcohol preparations is suitable for example chlorhexidine in 70% alcohol.
4 Cannulae.
5 Razor.
6 Clean paper towels and polythene sheet.
7 Fixative.

Choice of cannula

In an adult the smallest cannula likely to be adequate is an 18 gauge.

For large infusions one or more 14 gauge cannulae may be used. To some extent choice of cannula is a personal preference. However, polyvinylchloride (PVC) cannulae are more irritant than Teflon ones. Some controversy exists regarding the use of a cannula with a side port for injection. This injection port may act as a sump which cannot be cleaned prior to the injection procedure and a 55% incidence of contamination with pathogenic organisms at this site has been reported. It may be that organisms can be injected into the bloodstream without contamination of the cannula. In health a few bacteria in the bloodstream may be harmless but in an ill patient this is clearly unacceptable. Despite this, one such cannula with a side port (Venflon) has shown a similar incidence of phlebitis, positive cannula tip culture and bacteraemia as other cannulae.

Procedure

The doctor should explain the procedure to the patient and reassure him. The most suitable veins are those of the forearm avoiding sites close to the wrist and elbow since flexion may obstruct the flow of the infusion. It is advisable to remove the arm from the gown or other clothing and to shave the area if the patient is especially hirsute. A tourniquet or sphygmomanometer cuff can be used to obstruct the venous flow. The veins should be palpated. The junction point between two veins is a convenient access point.

The hands are washed and dried on a clean towel. Then the skin is prepared. 1% lignocaine may be injected through a fine needle to raise a wheal and provide local anaesthesia. Unfortunately this may to some extent obscure the anatomy. The vein should be stabilised with the left hand by traction on the skin towards the patients fingers. The cannula and needle are then inserted through the skin a few millimetres distal to the vein. As the vein is entered blood flashes back into the cannula. At this point the cannula can be advanced into the vein as the needle is withdrawn. The tourniquet is deflated and the infusion system connected. Blood spillage should be reduced to a minimum by pressure on the cannula tip within the vein as the needle is withdrawn and the infusion connected.

Fixation

Adhesive tape should be used to ensure fixation. The infusion tubing may be looped to the skin then the whole area with the exception of the injection port may be covered with broad elastoplast avoiding total encircling of the limb.

Problems

1 Venous access. It is not uncommon in an ill patient to find many damaged thrombosed veins due to previous infusions. In these circumstances it is helpful to ensure a vasodilated limb if necessary by placing the arm in warm water. A sphygmomanometer cuff accurately pumped up to between systolic and diastolic pressure will help. The patient is encouraged to clench his fist several times and gentle tapping over the vein will cause it to stand out. As far as possible veins on the dorsum of the hand should not be used. If an antecubital fossa vein is the only suitable one then insertion of a long central venous line should be considered. The basilic vein is a useful often overlooked site.

2 Thrombophlebitis. The puncture site becomes contaminated with bacteria and then infection within the lumen of the cannula extends to the vein. This is made worse if irritant fluids are infused. In most circumstances the bacteria arise from the patient's own skin and not from the infusion fluid. The use of bacterial filters to remove organisms from the infusion fluid has little effect on the incidence of thrombophlebitis. The cannula should be removed and a new one sited elsewhere.

3 Infusion fluid. Having sited the cannula it is essential to ensure that the fluid regime is clearly written up on the prescription chart and that it is appropriate for the patient. One of the commonest problems in management of i.v.i. is dehydration or overhydration.

4 Deep vein thrombosis. It has been shown by Janvrin that blood clots more readily when diluted with saline. Recently a trial in 60 patients undergoing routine laparotomy showed that 30% of the patients given an i.v.i. sustained a deep vein thrombosis (DVT) assessed by radioisotope scanning using ^{125}I fibrinogen uptake whereas only 7% of the patients who were not transfused had a DVT.

For most purposes of fluid administration manual drip regulation is considered adequate. However in paediatric practice, or in adults where fluid restriction is appropriate and for more accurate methods of fluid and drug administration automatic methods are required. One solution to this problem is to use a burette system loaded with the correct fluid volume to be infused over the next hour. An alternative is to use an infusion pump. These fall into two categories:

(a)   Drip counters
(b)   Volumetric infusion pumps.

Only volumetric infusion pumps are really accurate at low volumes. Also available are motorised syringes designed to give variable volumes of fluid over a number of hours. These are useful for continuous heparin or insulin administration.

CENTRAL VENOUS PRESSURE LINE

There are a few emergency circumstances where absence of peripheral veins necessitates cannulation of a central vein as a life saving procedure. More often however this is an elective undertaking.

Indications

Monitoring

Central venous pressure (CVP) varies with:

1   Venous blood volume.
2   Right ventricular function.
3   Venous tone.

Existing or anticipated large changes in blood volume are the commonest reason for CVP monitoring.

Administration of substances irritant to peripheral veins

Solutions of amino acids and concentrated carbohydrate used for parenteral nutrition are hypertonic, irritant to peripheral veins and must therefore be given into a central vein. Inotropic agents such as adrenaline produce profound constriction if administered through a peripheral vein. 25–50% Althesin infusions produce severe peripheral thrombophlebitis and should therefore be given into a central line. However at least one case of subclavian vein thrombosis has occurred.

Equipment

Insertion of a CVP line should be done with strict asepsis. A special pack is a great help and should contain ample towels and swabs. Skin preparation. An iodine preparation in spirit is suitable.

Catheters

Many varieties are available. The only recommended ones are those which use a cannula over a needle which is inserted into the vein, the needle withdrawn and the catheter threaded through the cannula. If a catheter is threaded directly through a sharp needle only a tiny amount of catheter withdrawal may result in shearing off the catheter. PVC catheters are relatively hard and have been associated with perforation of the right atrium or ventricle with fatal cardiac tamponade. Teflon catheters are less irritant and silicone coated ones are least likely to be associated with fibrin formation and subsequent bacterial colonisation. These are particularly suitable for long term parenteral nutrition.

Choice of site

The antecubital fossa veins may be used. The median basilic vein is preferable as a long catheter threaded via the cephalic vein will sometimes not go beyond the level of the clavipectoral fascia. The external jugular vein is not a recommended site as only 50% of catheters can be threaded to an intrathoracic position. The internal jugular vein has the advantage of being straight but its close proximity to the carotid artery is a disadvantage. The infraclavicular approach to the subclavian vein is now popular for long term cannulation as fixation is easy and the patient can be very mobile.

No attempt should be made to insert a cannula at a septic site. In the septicaemic patient a central catheter may provide a continuous source of bacteraemia. Blind cannulation of an invisible vein in the neck is not recommended in disorders of coagulation. There is a

danger of air embolus when the catheter enters the great veins in a
hypovolaemic patient. Measures to avoid this are essential.

Arm veins

Essentially the method is initially that for setting up a drip. The head
should be turned to the same side to compress the neck veins. The
catheter should be 70 cm or more in length for an adult. When the
tourniquet is released the proximal end of the catheter should be
kept low to avoid air embolism. About 75% of catheters should be
accurately placed using this technique.

Internal jugular vein

This vein runs behind the sternomastoid close to the lateral aspect
of the carotid artery.

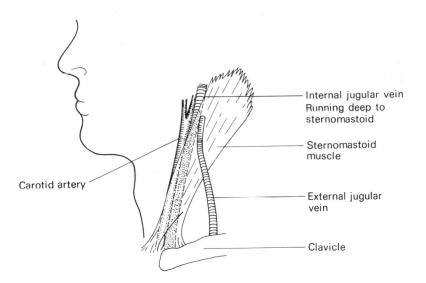

Internal jugular vein
Running deep to
sternomastoid

Sternomastoid
muscle

External jugular
vein

Carotid artery

Clavicle

Fig. 15.1   The position of the internal jugular vein.

The right internal jugular vein is easier for the right handed
operator and also avoids injury to the thoracic duct. The patient is

placed 20° head down with his head turned away from the side of cannulation. The point of entry is the midpoint of a line joining the mastoid process to the sternoclavicular junction. The carotid artery should be gently pulled medially and the needle with its cannula is attached to a syringe of saline. The needle should be at 30° to the skin and directed towards the feet slightly laterally from the mid-line. As the needle is advanced aspiration will confirm entry into the vein. The cannula is then inserted, the needle withdrawn and the catheter threaded through the cannula. It can then be connected to a bubble free infusion system. This route is associated with the highest number of correct placements (up to 99%).

Subclavian cannulation

The infraclavicular approach to the subclavian is now a popular site for CVP insertion.

The subclavian vein crosses the first rib behind the medial third of the clavicle to become intrathoracic. The patient is positioned as for internal jugular cannulation. A point 1–2 cm below the midpoint of

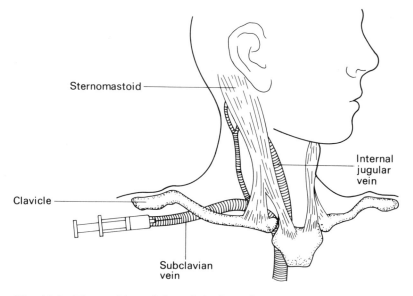

Fig. 15.2   The position of the subclavian vein.

the clavicle is marked. Using a long needle and cannula attached to a saline filled syringe the assembly is advanced along the under surface of the clavicle in the direction of the sternoclavicular junction. Aspiration of dark venous blood confirms successful subclavian puncture. The procedure is continued as already described. It may be necessary to depress the head of the humerus in order not to go too deeply. Occasionally a sandbag between the shoulders is helpful. This route may be associated with a rather high rate of catheter misplacement (5–25%). However fixation is much easier and allows greater patient mobility during long term use.

Procedure

The patient should be reassured and a full explanation of the procedure given. The operator should scrub up and wear gown, mask and gloves. The skin is then cleaned over a wide area and the chosen site surrounded with sterile towels. Local infiltration with 1% lignocaine is used unless the patient is receiving general anaesthesia.

Confirmation of catheter position

When the infusion fluid has been connected it should be lowered towards the floor. Back flow of blood confirms the intravascular position of the catheter tip. When the catheter is connected to a fluid manometer for recording the value of the CVP, oscillations of the fluid column in time with respiration and sometimes pulse rate confirm the intrathoracic position.

However a chest x-ray is mandatory following even an unsuccessful attempt at cannulation for two reasons:

(a)   To confirm the position of the catheter tip.
(b)   To exclude a pneumothorax. For this reason the chest x-ray should be taken in expiration.

Fixation

Many systems include an attachment for skin sutures which is invaluable for long term use in preventing accidental removal. An Opsite or similar plastic dressing which is transparent will allow inspection of the wound without additional manipulation, which

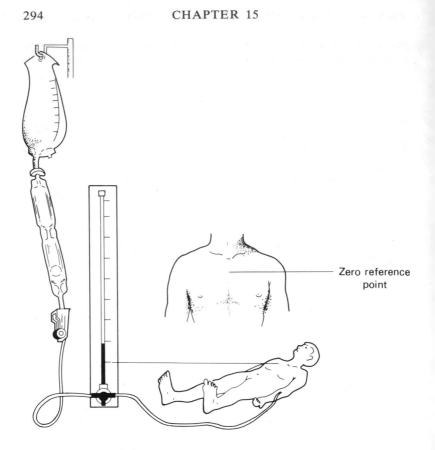

Fig. 15.3 Central venous pressure manometer.

may lead to contamination. The catheter must be very firmly attached to the skin.

Following insertion strict asepsis is necessary to avoid contamination. Drugs should preferably be injected through a peripheral line and taps excluded from the central line since these are a site of potential introduction of bacteria.

Zeroing

The author uses the sternal Angle of Louis as a reference point. Others prefer the midclavicular line. It is essential that the reference point is clearly defined. The normal CVP as measured from the Angle of Louis is −3 to +3 cm water.

Problems

Immediate

1 Damage to large vessels in the neck. Carotid or subclavian artery puncture may occur accidentally. Firm pressure should be applied to the carotid if this is punctured keeping a watch on the pulse rate for bradycardia. Veins may also be perforated resulting in substantial haemorrhage.
2 Pneumothorax, haemothorax. Either of these may be fatal. The importance of the post-insertion chest x-ray cannot be over-emphasised.
3 Thoracic duct injury.
4 Phrenic nerve damage.

If misplaced catheters are not recognised irritant fluids may be infused extravenously resulting in tissue damage.

Throughout

1 Air embolus.
2 Catheter detachment.
3 Cardiac arrythmia.

Late complications

1 Sepsis including bacterial endocarditis.
2 Central vein thrombosis. This is commonest during prolonged cannulation for parenteral nutrition.
3 Myocardial perforation and tamponade.

The overall complication rate for neck vein cannulation is about 15%. Unexplained fever for 12 hours is an indication to remove the central line and culture its tip. Scrupulous attention to detail is essential to reduce the complication rate in this increasingly commonly performed procedure.

Cannulation of peripheral arteries and insertion of a Swan Ganz catheter are beyond the scope of this book. Information is supplied elsewhere.

Further Reading

General

BERLYNE G. M. (1980) *A Course in Clinical Disorders of Body Fluids and Electrolytes.* Blackwell Scientific Publications, Oxford.
CAROL H. J. and OH M. S. (1978) *Water, Electrolyte and Acid Base Balance; diagnosis and management.* Lippincott, Philadelphia.
MAXWELL M. H. and KLEEMAN C. R. (1979) *Clinical Disorders of Fluid and Electrolyte Metabolism,* 3e. McGraw-Hill, New York.

Specific

Metabolic response to trauma

CUTHBERTSON D. P. (1972) Protein requirements after injury, quality and quantity. In Wilkinson *Parenteral Nutrition.* Churchill Livingstone, Edinburgh.
MOORE F. D. (1959) *Metabolic Care of the Surgical Patient.* W. B. Saunders, Philadelphia.
MOORE R. A., SMITH R. F. *et al* (1981) Sex and Surgical Stress. *Anaesthesia* **36,** 263.

Fluid balance in the surgical patient

JANVRIN S. B., DAVIES G. and GREENHALGH R. M. (1980) Postoperative deep vein thrombosis caused by intravenous fluids during surgery. *British Journal of Surgery* **67,** 690.

Renal disease

BEVAN D. R. (1979) *Renal Function in Anaesthesia and Surgery.* Academic Press, London.
BLACK D. and JONES N. F. (1979) *Renal Disease,* 4e. Blackwell Scientific Publications. Oxford.
ESPINEL C. H. and GREGORY A. W. (1980) Differential diagnosis of acute renal failure. *Clinical nephrology* **13** (2), 73–79.

Parenteral nutrition

CAHILL G. F. (1976) Starvation in Man. *Clinical Endocrinology and Metabolism* **5,** 397.
LEE H. A. (1974) *Parenteral Nutrition in Acute Medical Illness.* Academic Press, London.

Acid base balance

BRYANT M. T. T. (1977) Gases stored in disposable syringes. A study of changes in their concentration. *Anaesthesia* **32**, 784.

SYKES M. K. (1975) The management of acid base balance. In *Anaesthesia Rounds,* Number 9. I.C.I. Ltd.

Specific problems: burns

MUIR I. F. K. and BARCLAY T. L. (1974) *Burns and their Treatment,* 2e. Lloyd Luke, London.

SETTLE J. A. D. (1974) Urine output in burns. *Burns* **1** (1), 23–42.

Practicalities of setting up infusion lines

GEORGE R. J. D. (1980) Practical procedures. How to insert a flotation catheter. *British Journal of Hospital Medicine* **23** (3), 296.

PETERS J. L., FISHER C. and MEHTA S. (1980) Intravenous stopcocks and injection ports. *Lancet* ii, 701.

WILLATTS S. (1980) Practical procedures. How to cannulate a peripheral artery. *British Journal of Hospital Medicine* **23** (6), 628.

Index

298